THE
BIBLE STORY
LIBRARY

**The Holy Scriptures retold in
story form for the young and as an explanation
and commentary for all, based on traditional texts and
illustrated with the most famous Biblical art.**

VOLUME SIX

*From
The wars of Judah
To
The Maccabees*

Edited by TURNER HODGES
with the assistance of ELIZABETH MACLEAN
Designed and produced by DONALD D. WOLF
with the assistance of MARGOT L. WOLF

Josiah set out to destroy the idols and the heathen altars throughout the land. He ordered his soldiers to tear them down wherever they might be.

99

The story of the wars of Judah

MANASSEH BECAME KING OF JUDAH when he was only twelve years old, but in those days a youth of twelve was more a man than a boy.

Unfortunately, Manasseh was very evil. Instead of worshiping the Lord, as his father had done, he worshiped the sun and the moon and the stars as gods. He built altars to these false gods and led the people of Judah into heathen worship once again.

The Lord tried to warn Manasseh and the people, by sending prophets to them, but the people did not want to hear.

Then the Lord let the Assyrian army attack the people of Judah, and the Assyrians captured Manasseh. He had been hiding among the bushes, but they found him and bound him with heavy chains. He was taken to Babylon, and while he was imprisoned there he repented of his sins and prayed with all his heart to the Lord for forgiveness. The Lord heard him and allowed him to return to Jerusalem. Then Manasseh realized that he had been wrong in worshiping idols, and he commanded that all the idols be removed and their altars destroyed. He repaired the altar of the Lord and offered sacrifices on it.

Manasseh was king over Judah longer than any other ruler. He reigned for fifty-five years, and when he died his son Ammon became king.

Ammon was an idolator and a wicked king. His reign lasted for only two years, and then some of his ministers entered into a conspiracy against him and killed him. Ammon's son, Josiah, who was just eight years old, became the next king.

More than two hundred years before the birth of Josiah, a prophet in Israel had told Jeroboam, first king of Israel, that one day a king of Judah would go to Israel and burn the bones of men on the heathen altar. This king was Josiah. When he became king the ten tribes who lived in the northern kingdom of Israel had been carried away, and the kingdom of Israel no longer existed, but still Josiah fulfilled the prophecy.

Josiah began to serve the Lord while he was still a boy. When he became king he set out to destroy the idols and the heathen altars throughout the land. He ordered his soldiers to tear them down wherever they might be. Josiah also set men at work to repair the Temple, for it had been neglected during the years before Josiah's reign.

While the workmen were repairing the Temple, a high priest found the book of the law of God, the book written by Moses when the Lord gave him the law. The book consisted of a great roll of parchment, or thin sheepskin, which was used for paper then, and instead of being printed it was all written by hand. Printing and bookbinding had not yet been invented.

The people had been instructed to listen while the laws were read aloud

Manasseh sins by offering sacrifices to an idol (the statue above the altar).

451

to them once every seven years, but this had been neglected by the wicked people of Judah for a long time. Even Josiah had never seen the laws, but now the high priest read the laws to him.

Josiah then learned what punishments the Lord had promised to send if the people failed to obey His laws, and Josiah knew that for many years the laws had been ignored.

"What is going to happen to us?" he wailed. "We have not done the things God has commanded us to do, and He will certainly punish us."

Then he asked a high priest to consult a prophetess named Huldah, to find out what the Lord would do to punish the people of Judah.

"The Lord will punish Jerusalem and its people, who have not obeyed His laws," said Huldah. "However, because King Josiah has prayed for his people, and has turned back again into the way of the Lord, the punishment will not come during his lifetime."

After Josiah had heard the words of the prophetess he gathered the priests, the Levites, and the people all together and read them the words of the law. They all then promised to obey the commandments of the Lord.

All the vessels that had been used in offering sacrifices to the heathen god Baal were destroyed, and the priests of Baal were sent away.

Josiah then went to Bethel, where Jeroboam had heard the prophecy concerning the altar.

When Josiah reached Bethel, he saw some sepulchers, or coffins, on a hillside near the altar of Baal. From the sepulchers he took some of the bones of dead men and burned them on the altar, just as the prophet had foretold to Jeroboam. From that time, the altar would be considered permanently defiled, or unclean, and unfit for any kind of religious sacrifices. (Dead men's bones were considered extremely unclean in Biblical times, and to touch anything with them would make that thing unclean also.) Even worshipers of idols would have nothing to do with an altar so defiled.

Sins of the people Since the death of Hezekiah, the people had failed to keep the feast of the Passover, which was one of the Lord's commands. Josiah now reëstablished this feast. The people obeyed his commands and attended the feast, but they were not sincere worshipers of the Lord. They still had faith in their idols.

Jeremiah, a great prophet of God, tried to tell them that the Lord would

Josiah defiles the heathen altars by burning on them the bones of men.

punish them if they did not cease their evil ways, but they paid no attention. He reminded them of all they had received from God, and of their deliverance from Egypt, but still they scorned his advice. They even wanted to kill Jeremiah, but the Lord saved him.

Death of Josiah The king of Egypt now entered the land of Judah with a large army, and Josiah assembled his forces to fight him. "I have not come to fight your people," said the king in a message to Josiah. "I am here to make war against the king of Assyria. Return with your armies to your own home."

Instead of going home, however, Josiah changed clothing with another man, so that no one would recognize him by his royal robes, and he went into battle. Soon an arrow of one of the Egyptian soldiers struck him, and he told his servants to take him out of the battle.

"I am badly wounded," he said.

The Judeans placed their injured king in a chariot and removed him from the battle, but he died very shortly.

453

After the death of Josiah, his son Jehoahaz became king of Judah. But Jehoahaz reigned for only three months; then the king of Egypt attacked Jerusalem and captured him. He put Jehoahaz in chains and carried him to Egypt, where he remained a prisoner until he died. Pharaoh (the Egyptian king) made Jehoiakim, the brother of Jehoahaz, king of Israel next, but he compelled Jehoiakim to pay a high tribute in money.

The land of Judah was greatly weakened at that time, and the king of Egypt had taken so much money there was not a great deal left. The land was so weak that when the king of Babylon attacked the army of Judah, Jehoiakim was unable to resist. Instead he promised to be a subject of Nebuchadnezzar, king of Babylon. So all the people of Judah became subjects of Nebuchadnezzar.

100

The story of the prophet Jeremiah

EHOIAKIM HAD BEEN KING for a little over three years when the Lord spoke to the prophet Jeremiah and told him to write down in a book the punishments in store for the Israelites. These punishments would come only if the people failed to repent of their sins, and to live righteously. There was still time for them to repent and be forgiven by the Lord.

Jeremiah then approached a man named Baruch, who was called a scribe (which meant he knew how to write). Very few people other than some priests could write in those days.

Baruch wrote down all the words Jeremiah spoke, exactly as he spoke them. It was a large book when it was finished, and it contained a complete list of the punishments the Lord promised to inflict on the people if they did not repent.

"Now take the book to the Temple and read it aloud to the people, so that everyone will know what the Lord has said," Jeremiah told Baruch. The scribe did this, and the princes in the king's palace sent for Baruch and asked him to read the book to them also. When Baruch had finished reading, and they had heard all the list of punishments the Lord had in store for them and their people, they were very frightened.

"How did it happen that you wrote such things?" they asked Baruch.

"Jeremiah said all these things," Baruch answered. "As he spoke, I simply wrote down what he said."

"We must go and tell the king about this," said the princes. "But you and Jeremiah had better go and hide. The king may be very angry and try to harm you both."

The princes told King Jehoiakim about the book, as they had said they would do, and he sent a servant to fetch it to him. The king was seated beside an open fire on his hearth, and the servant read it to him there. As soon as the servant had finished reading a few pages, the king took a knife and cut them off, and tossed them into the fire. He listened a while longer, and then burned up the next section as the servant finished reading it. He continued in this manner, listening a while, and then burning up the part he had heard, until the entire book was destroyed by the fire. Some of the princes begged him not to do it, but he paid no attention. He cared nothing about the great trouble that would be visited on the people; he was only angry at Jeremiah and Baruch for having written the book. He sent soldiers to imprison them, but the Lord did not allow the soldiers to find the two men.

It did no good for the king to destroy the book, because the Lord told Jeremiah to repeat what he had said before, and Baruch wrote it again on another roll of parchment paper. This time the Lord told Jeremiah more things to include in the book.

The people of Judah hated Jeremiah for telling them of their sins, as all guilty persons dislike to be told of their guilt.

"I have done no evil," said Jeremiah, "and yet the people all hate me."

The Lord then promised Jeremiah that when the enemies of Jerusalem came to capture the city they would not harm Jeremiah.

Jehoiakim died after he had reigned for eleven years, and his son Jehoiachin became king. He ruled for only three months in Jerusalem, however, because King Nebuchadnezzar of Babylon attacked the city once again. Jehoiachin promised to live in submission to Nebuchadnezzar, and once again the king of Babylon went into the Temple to remove treasures and golden vessels. As he had done the last time, he went to the king's palace and took the king's treasures also. He did not stop there, however, as he had before. He took the king, his mother, his wives, and all the princes of Judah, and made them captives in Babylon. He also captured all the builders and carpenters and strong soldiers in Jerusalem and took them to Babylon.

There were many of the people of Judah taken as captives to Babylon, but there were still some left in their own land. Jeremiah wrote a letter to those who had been taken to Babylon. He told them to try to live con-

Jeremiah dictates his prophecies to the scribe Baruch.

tentedly in that land, because the Lord had said they would be there for
seventy years as servants to the king of Babylon. Jeremiah told them that
they should build houses for themselves, and plant good gardens, and in

457

general live normal lives. If they repented of all their past sins, and prayed for forgiveness, the Lord would pardon them at the end of the seventy years and would let them return to their own land.

Nebuchadnezzar made Jehoiachin's brother, Zedekiah, king over the people left in the land of Judah; but Zedekiah was little more than a servant to Nebuchadnezzar. After a short time, when Nebuchadnezzar had returned to his own land, Zedekiah rebelled. Nebuchadnezzar then besieged Jerusalem with his great army of Chaldeans, and no one could get in or out of the city.

Jeremiah the prophet was shut up in Jerusalem with the rest of the people, and King Zedekiah sent word to him, asking that he pray to the Lord for the safety of the city.

Jeremiah had to tell Zedekiah what the Lord told him to say.

"I cannot tell you that the Lord will save your city," said Jeremiah. "The Lord has said that the Chaldeans will capture Jerusalem and set fire to it. Still, if the people will bear the Lord's punishment willingly, and will go out to King Nebuchadnezzar and become his servants, then they will not be put to death. Whoever will stop fighting, and go out willingly to surrender, will be spared. All who stay in the city will be killed either in battle, by famine, or by disease."

The Lord had said these things, and they would therefore come true.

"Why do we not have Jeremiah put to death?" said some of the princes. "He frightens the people with the dreadful things he says."

"Do with him anything you choose!" said Zedekiah.

With that, the princes seized Jeremiah and lowered him by ropes into a deep pit that had a soft, muddy bottom. The pit was in a strong prison, but this part had no floor and Jeremiah's feet sank deeply into the mire.

One of the king's officers was alarmed when he learned what the princes had done to Jeremiah, and he spoke to the king.

"Your majesty," he said, "these men have acted very wrongly in putting Jeremiah into that dungeon. He will starve to death there."

"Very well," said Zedekiah. "Take some men and remove Jeremiah from the pit, so that he will not die there."

The officer selected some men to go with him. He took several pieces of old clothing and rags, which they lowered to Jeremiah on long ropes.

"Make pads of these pieces of clothing and rags, and put them under

Jeremiah is pulled out of the dungeon.

The destruction and burning of Jerusalem by the Chaldeans.

the ropes by which we will pull you up, so that the rope will not cut into your flesh," the officer told him.

Jeremiah did so, and the men pulled him up by means of the ropes, and released him from the pit. They did not set him free, however, but placed him in another part of the prison.

After Jeremiah had been removed from the pit, the king sent for him and they talked in the entrance to the Temple, so that no one would hear what was said.

"I have a question for you," said the king. "Give me an honest answer, please."

"If I answer you honestly," said Jeremiah, "will you promise me that you will not have me put to death, even if the answer does not please you?"

"I promise solemnly that I will not have you put to death," said the king, "nor will I turn you over to men who want to kill you."

Then Jeremiah spoke.

"I know what your question is, because the Lord has told me what to say," he declared. "If you will surrender to the king of Babylon, and agree to serve him, then neither you nor any of your family will be put to death, and the city will not be burned."

"But I am afraid that if I surrender to the Chaldeans they will turn me over to the people of Judah, who now are against me," said the king.

"The Chaldeans will not give you to them," said Jeremiah. "Please obey the command of the Lord, so that you may be spared. If you refuse, your wives and children will be given over to the Chaldeans, you will not escape yourself, and the city will be burned."

King Zedekiah did not obey the command of the Lord and surrender to the king of Babylon. As a result, the Chaldeans besieged the city for eighteen months, until there was nothing left inside the city walls for the people to eat. One night Zedekiah fled from Jerusalem with his family and with as much of his army as he could gather together, but the Chaldeans caught him and took him to the king of Babylon. Nebuchadnezzar killed Zedekiah's two sons and put out Zedekiah's eyes. Then he bound the blinded king with chains and took him to Babylon, where he held him in prison until he died.

The city of Jerusalem was burned and the walls around it were broken down. Nebuchadnezzar took all the treasures that were still left in the city, and carried away the people who were still alive in Jerusalem, leaving just a few men to work in the fields and vineyards. Nebuchadnezzar made a man called Gedaliah governor over the few who were left.

101

The story of the end of Judah

EDEKIAH WAS THE LAST KING of Judah, and that kingdom was ended when Nebuchadnezzar took its people away into captivity in Babylon.

The kingdom had lasted in all for three hundred and forty-four years after the death of Solomon. During that time it had nineteen kings and one queen. Only five of these were good kings who served the Lord. Even the good kings were not enough to make the people live righteously, however, and though the Lord sent prophets to warn them of what would happen to them, the people did not listen. Finally, the Lord did as He had said He would do if they did not better their ways. He took the land of Canaan away from the people of Judah.

The Lord had promised Jeremiah that the Chaldeans would not illtreat him after the city of Jerusalem had been captured and burned. The promise was fulfilled immediately after the fall of the city, when the king of Babylon spoke to the captain of his army.

"Do not harm Jeremiah under any circumstances," the king ordered. "Release him from prison, where the men of Judah have left him, and let him go wherever he wishes."

The captain did as his king had commanded.

"If you wish to go to Babylon with me, you may come," the captain said to Jeremiah. "However, you need not come if you do not want to. You may stay here or go wherever you choose. Also, if you like, you may go and live with Gedaliah, who has been made governor."

The captain then gave Jeremiah money and food and let him go. Jeremiah decided to live with Gedaliah, because he wanted to remain with those of his people who were still in the land of Canaan.

The Jews mourn for their destroyed city of Jerusalem: Doré's engraving.

After the Chaldeans captured the people of Jerusalem, some who had escaped fled into the desert and some went into other countries around Judah. When news reached them that Nebuchadnezzar had left some of the people still in the land, they returned to Judah. They could not go back to Jerusalem, because that city had been destroyed, but they went to Mizpeh, where the governor appointed by Nebuchadnezzar lived. Gedaliah was a kind man, and a good governor. He welcomed the returning Judeans kindly.

"Do not be afraid to come back and live on your own land," he said. "If you plant crops, and harvest your grain, and give your allegiance to the king of Babylon, no one will harm you."

With this reassurance, the people came back and cultivated the land. Their crops were good, and they grew plenty of fruit and grain for themselves.

One day some men visited Gedaliah and told him of a plot against him.

"Do you know that the king of the Ammonites has sent one of the princes of Judah to kill you?" they asked. "His name is Ishmael."

One of the men then took Gedaliah aside.

"Let me go and kill this Ishmael," he begged. "No one will know."

Gedaliah did not believe these men, and to the one who had asked permission to kill Ishmael he spoke sharply.

"You most certainly must not kill Ishmael," he said. "I do not believe that anyone wants to kill me!"

Gedaliah was wrong; the men had spoken the truth. A short time later, Ishmael and ten other men visited Gedaliah's house, pretending that they had stopped only to ask for food before continuing their journey. In those days, a man always offered food to a traveler who stopped at his house, because there were no hotels or inns.

Gedaliah was generous and gave the travelers food, but after they had eaten his food they killed him, and Ishmael fled to the land of the Ammonites.

After Gedaliah's death, the people still living in Judah were afraid that the king of Babylon would come and punish them for the death of his governor. In their fear they approached Jeremiah and asked him to pray to the Lord for them.

"I will pray for you," said Jeremiah. "But whatever the Lord tells me I will tell you, even if I feel that you will not be pleased at the answer."

"We will do whatever the Lord commands," they said.

Jeremiah then prayed to the Lord, and after ten days the Lord answered him and told him what to say to the people.

"The Lord has told me what I shall say to you," said Jeremiah to the people. "The Lord says that if you stay in this land, He will take care of you. You do not need to be afraid of the king of Babylon, because the Lord will make him kind to you. But if you go to Egypt, for fear that there will be war and famine in Canaan, you will suffer and will never see your own land again."

The people did not believe Jeremiah.

"You are not telling us the truth!" they cried. "You want us to stay here so that the Chaldeans can come and kill us all, or make us captives in Babylon!"

So once again the people did not believe the words of the prophet that the Lord had sent; and all the people, taking Jeremiah with them, moved out of Canaan into the land of Egypt.

Then the prophecy of Isaiah, made more than a hundred years before that time, was fulfilled—the land of Judah was left lonely and deserted, with weeds and briars growing everywhere, and filled with empty houses where no one lived any more.

102

The story of the prophet Ezekiel

A T THE TIME WHEN JEREMIAH was serving as prophet of the Lord in Jerusalem, another man was doing the same thing for the people who had been taken captive by Nebuchadnezzar and carried to Babylon.

This man was Ezekiel, and he had been taken as captive to Babylon at the same time that Nebuchadnezzar had captured King Jehoiakim, his mother, his wives, and the princes of Judah.

The Lord appeared to Ezekiel in a vision, when the prophet had been in Babylon for a little more than four years. In that vision the Lord commanded Ezekiel to make a map of Jerusalem on a flat, earthenware tile and place it inside an iron pan, to symbolize the walls about the city of Jerusalem. On the outside of the iron pan he was to make a model of the forts of attacking soldiers, to indicate that the city was going to be under siege.

Ezekiel was then told to lie down on the ground beside this map of Jerusalem and stay there for many days. During those days he was to eat only a small quantity of coarse bread and drink only a small amount of water.

This was meant to tell the captive Israelites in Babylon of the fate that was in store for Jerusalem, when it would be under siege and the people in the city would have very little to eat.

Then the Lord told Ezekiel to take a razor, such as was used by barbers, and shave off the hair of his head and beard.

He should then divide the hair into three equal parts, weighing each part on a scale to make certain the three were exactly equal.

Ezekiel prophesying.

Ezekiel was then told to go to the place where he had left the map of Jerusalem, and burn one part of his hair there, as the city was later burned. Another part of his hair he was to cut up into small pieces with his knife, to symbolize the people who would be killed in battle against the forces of Nebuchadnezzar. The third part of the hair he was to hold up in his hand, and let the wind scatter it in all directions, to symbolize the way that all those left of the people of Judah would be scattered.

A year later, Ezekiel had another vision. This time it seemed that a great force lifted him by a lock of his hair and carried him from Babylon to Jerusalem. There he was told to look toward the north. Ezekiel looked and saw an idol set up near the Lord's altar.

There was still a further example of the people's wickedness that the Lord showed Ezekiel in his vision. Ezekiel was taken to the outer wall of the Temple and told to dig a hole through which he could creep inside and see what was going on. Ezekiel in his vision did so. He saw the elders of Israel burning incense to pictures of unclean beasts and to idols worshiped by the sinning people of Israel.

The Lord told Ezekiel that the people believed the Lord could not see them, because they were behind closed doors and worshiped their heathen idols in secret.

Another group of people, which the Lord showed to Ezekiel in his vision, were worshiping the sun as it rose in the sky. The Lord told Ezekiel how angry He was at all these things.

When the vision was over, Ezekiel thought that he was lifted again by a great force and removed from Jerusalem, where he had seen all these awful things, and taken back to the place from which he had started, a place by the river Chebar in Babylon.

Afterward Ezekiel told the people of Judah who were captives in Babylon what he had seen, but they did not believe him. They preferred to believe their heathen idols' prophets. The idols' prophets had said that the people of Jerusalem would not suffer and that their city would not be captured by the king of Babylon.

Ezekiel was given many instructions by the Lord. He was told to act like a man who was trying to escape without being noticed, to represent the attempt of King Zedekiah to escape from Jerusalem. He was told to act like a man who was afraid as he ate and drank that someone would take

Ezekiel's vision: He sees a chariot drawn by four manlike, winged creatures.

his food away from him before he had satisfied his hunger. This was to represent the fear that would be suffered by the Judeans in Jerusalem when their enemies came to attack them. Those enemies would surely attack, the Lord told Ezekiel, and they would destroy the cities of Judah, leaving them lonely and desolate, and they would carry away the people as captives.

On the day that the king of Babylon opened his attack against the city of Jerusalem, the Lord told Ezekiel to write down the date so that the people would always remember it. Ezekiel was told by the Lord of the siege that was taking place many miles away—long before news of the battle had time to travel so far.

Ezekiel told the people what the Lord had let him see, and they questioned him further.

"If the Lord is going to punish us, and destroy us for our sins, what can we do to save ourselves?" they asked.

"There is just one thing you can do," said Ezekiel. "Repent of your sins and live according to the laws of God. You know the Lord does not take

Ezekiel's vision: He is told to speak to the bones and restore life to them.

pleasure in punishing the evil men of this world. The Lord wants to see His people turn from their wickedness, so that He will not need to punish them."

Many months later, one of the men who had escaped from Jerusalem reached the place where Ezekiel and the other captives were staying.

"Jerusalem has been taken by the King of Babylon," said the man.

When the captives heard this they knew that everything Ezekiel had told them was true. Their false prophets had said that Jerusalem would not be taken, but Ezekiel, the prophet of the Lord, had said it would be.

Then the Lord made it clear to Ezekiel that although the people of Israel had to be punished, they were not to be entirely destroyed. They would be punished for a time; but some day, when they had truly repented, the Lord would once again take them for His people.

The Lord showed Ezekiel another wonderful vision. The prophet told the people later what he had seen.

"It seemed that I was carried to a valley filled with dead men's bones— old and dry bones," said Ezekiel. "Then the Lord told me to speak to the dry bones and tell them that it was the command of the Lord that flesh should come on them again, and the breath of life should return to their bodies, and they should live."

Then Ezekiel explained the meaning of that vision.

"The people of Israel are like those dry bones," he said. "They have lost all hope of happiness, or of seeing their own land again. But just as the Lord raised the dry bones and brought them back to life, He will raise up the people of Israel and take them back to the land of Canaan."

There was one further demonstration of the Lord's power. Ezekiel took two sticks and wrote on one the name "Judah" and on the other the name "Israel." As he held the sticks close together, they grew together in his hand and became a single stick.

"But what is the meaning of this wonder of the Lord?" the people asked.

"The Lord means that when the people of Israel return to the land of Canaan they will no longer be divided into two nations but will be all one people," said Ezekiel.

Jeremiah had prophesied that the Israelites would remain as captives in Babylon for seventy years, and then would return to Canaan. This happened as he said, but this return was not the one predicted by Ezekiel. After the Babylonian captivity was over, the people who returned to Canaan sinned again and the Lord was angry. Thereafter they were scattered throughout the world, as they are even today.

In one of his visions, Ezekiel saw the Temple rebuilt and measured it.

471

103

The story of Daniel and the dream

WHEN KING NEBUCHADNEZZAR was in Jerusalem, he told his chief officer to look over the princes of the land and select some of the most promising youths to be taught the language and customs of the Chaldeans.

"Find young men who are strong and handsome, with no bodily defects," he instructed the officer. "I want only the most intelligent, because I intend to make them my personal servants and take them to the palace with me."

Among the youths selected were four named Daniel, Hananiah, Mishael, and Azariah. The chief officer gave them Chaldean names, by which they were to be known in the city of Babylon. Daniel was called Belteshazzar; Hananiah became Shadrach; Mishael's name was changed to Meshach; and Azariah was known as Abednego.

They were taken to Babylon and teachers were assigned to instruct them in the wisdom and language of the Chaldeans. During their period of training, the king sent meat and wine to them from his own table.

However, Daniel and the three other young men did not want to eat the food prepared for the king's table. The Chaldeans worshiped idols and offered sacrifices to them, afterward eating the meat of the sacrifice. They also drank wine that had been used as offerings to idols. Daniel did not want to offend the Lord by eating food that was unclean by the Lord's law.

"We should not eat the king's food," said Daniel to Shadrach, Meshach, and Abednego. "We should not drink his wine."

"No, we should not," the other young men agreed. "What can we do?"

"We will speak to the officer who is in charge of such things," said Daniel, and when the man came again to see that they had food to eat, Daniel spoke to him.

"We would like your permission not to eat the food the king sends," said Daniel.

Although the officer had grown very fond of Daniel, he did not dare to grant that request.

"If you don't eat," he said, "you will grow thin and pale, and the king will have me put to death for not giving you the food as he commanded."

"I have a suggestion," said Daniel. "Give us only vegetables to eat, and water to drink, for just ten days. If there is any sign that we become thin or pale at the end of that time, you may give us whatever food you wish, and we will eat it, so that you will not risk punishment."

This request seemed reasonable, and was granted. For ten days the four young men ate only vegetables, and drank only water, and at the end of that time they were the strongest and healthiest-looking men of all those who had eaten the food from the king's table.

The Lord helped them all to gain a great deal of knowledge and wisdom, and He taught Daniel to interpret dreams.

After they had studied for three years, the four young Israelites were taken to the palace of the king. Nebuchadnezzar found that these four were wiser and more learned than any of the other wise men in his kingdom. He was greatly pleased with them.

Nebuchadnezzar's forgotten dream One night Nebuchadnezzar had a dream that troubled him so much he could not sleep afterward. "I must know what that dream meant!" he exclaimed, and he ordered his attendants to call all the wise men in Babylon to the palace.

They assembled and stood before him.

"I have had a dream and it worries me. I have called you so that you may interpret it for me," said the king.

"Tell us your dream, your majesty," said the wise men.

"I cannot," the king confessed. "Much as it troubled me, I cannot remember it now. It has gone from my mind. It is up to you wise men to tell me what the dream was that I have forgotten, and then interpret it for me."

"But no man can do that!" exclaimed the wise men. "Tell us the dream, and we can interpret. But we cannot tell you your dream, if you have even forgotten it yourself!"

Daniel interprets the dream of King Nebuchadnezzar.

The king was very angry and gave orders for all the wise men of Babylon to be put to death. This would include Daniel and his three friends, Shadrach, Meshach, and Abednego, for they were among the wise men of the land. They had not been called with the others, however, to go before the king, and the first they knew of the order was when the king's servant came to them with his orders to kill them.

"Why does the king suddenly wish to kill all his wise men?" asked Daniel. The officer told Daniel what had happened, and Daniel went immediately to the king's palace.

"Instead of having all your wise men killed because they could not tell you your dream, allow me a little time, your majesty, and I will come back and tell you all that you wish to know," said Daniel.

The king then stopped the order for the killing of the wise men, to allow Daniel some time.

Daniel left the king and returned to where his three friends were waiting. He explained the situation, and asked them all to pray to the Lord for help. Then he and the three others prayed, and the Lord answered their prayers. He let Daniel know the dream, and also its interpretation, and Daniel went back to Nebuchadnezzar.

"Can you tell me the dream I have forgotten, and give me its interpretation?" the king demanded.

"No wise man on earth could tell the king what he had dreamed and forgotten. Only God could do that," said Daniel. "God has told me of your dream, so that I might tell you, and so that you will know that He is the true God."

Then Daniel told Nebuchadnezzar the forgotten dream.

Nebuchadnezzar had dreamed that he saw a great statue, with a head of gold, arms of silver, and body of brass. The statue's legs were iron and his feet part iron and part clay.

The head of gold meant Nebuchadnezzar's kingdom, because that was the greatest and richest on earth. The other materials in the rest of the image symbolized new but weaker kingdoms that would arise after Nebuchadnezzar's death.

Next, in the dream, a great rock fell from the mountain and shattered the feet of the statue, so that the rest of it fell down and splintered into tiny fragments—pieces as fine as dust, and so small that the wind blew them away. After the statue had been broken in the dream, Daniel continued, the rock that had fallen on it grew larger and larger, until it filled all the earth. Daniel next explained what the falling rock meant, and its growing large enough to fill the entire earth.

"The rock is the kingdom of the Christ, for it will break into pieces all the other kingdoms in the world. This kingdom will never be broken, but will grow as the rock grew in your dream and will someday fill all the earth."

Then Nebuchadnezzar knew that the God of Daniel was the God of gods and the King of kings. Nebuchadnezzar gave Daniel great honors and made him chief of the wise men. To please Daniel, he also gave his three friends high positions.

104

The story of the prophets in the fiery furnace

ING NEBUCHADNEZZAR BUILT a great statue of gold and set it up on a plain. He then sent for all the rulers of his kingdom —the priests, the judges, the princes, the governors, and the captains—and assembled them all in the field in front of the statue. Then one of the king's servants made an announcement to the crowd, calling out to them all in a loud voice.

"This is the command of your king, Nebuchadnezzar," he cried. "As soon as you hear the sound of the harp, the flute, the trumpet, and all kinds of other music, you must fall down and worship the golden statue that Nebuchadnezzar, the king, has set up. Anyone who refuses to bow down and worship will be cast into the fiery furnace."

Then the king ordered the musicians to play, and when the people heard the sound of music they all bowed down and worshiped the idol, as the king had commanded.

However, Shadrach, Meshach, and Abednego did not bow down to worship the idol; because God's commandment forbids the worship of idols.

Some of the Chaldeans went quickly to the king and complained about the three men. Nebuchadnezzar had Shadrach, Meshach and Abednego brought before him.

"Is it true that you did not bow down and worship, as I commanded everyone to do?" he asked them.

"It is true, your majesty," they answered calmly.

"I will give you another chance," said Nebuchadnezzar. "When you hear again the sound of music, bow down and worship the golden image which I have set up. If you do not, you will be cast into the furnace and your God cannot save you then!"

Shadrach, Meshach and Abednego stand unharmed in the fiery furnace.

Shadrach, Meshach, and Abednego answered the king without fear.

"If you decide to cast us into the fiery furnace, our God can certainly save us if He chooses to do so. If He were to let us burn, still we will not worship an idol."

Nebuchadnezzar was furious. He ordered his servants to make the furnace seven times as hot as it had been before. They built the fire to a roaring inferno, so that it seemed nothing could withstand its searing flames. Then Nebuchadnezzar ordered his soldiers to bind Shadrach, Meshach, and Abednego, fully clothed, and cast them into the furnace.

To cast the three men into the flames, the soldiers had to go close to the furnace, and the heat from it killed them all. Shadrach, Meshach and Abednego fell down, bound, into the midst of the fire. Soon, however, they stood up and walked unharmed in the fire, for the Lord did not allow it to burn them.

Nebuchadnezzar suddenly gasped with alarm.

"Quickly, tell me!" he said to the people standing next to him. "Did we put the three men in the fire?"

"Yes, your majesty," he was answered.

"But I can see four men walking about in the midst of the flames, unharmed!" gasped Nebuchadnezzar. "The fourth man looks as if he is the Son of God!"

Then Nebuchadnezzar called to the men in the fire and told them to come out, quickly. Shadrach, Meshach, and Abednego came out, and all the people who were gathered there saw that there was not a hair of their heads burned by the fire—nor was their clothing scorched, nor was there any smell of fire about them.

After he had witnessed this great miracle, Nebuchadnezzar gave blessings in the name of the God of Shadrach, Meshach, and Abednego. He knew then that their God was the only true God.

"And I make here and now a law, and a decree," he said. "No one in this land shall speak evil of the God of Shadrach, Meshach, and Abednego. Anyone who does so will be destroyed, and his house torn down."

After that, the three young men were made greater and more important than ever in Babylon.

Nebuchadnezzar's madness Nebuchadnezzar continued to rule in Babylon for many years, and everything went well for him. He felt so sure of his strength and power that he forgot God. God was displeased with him, and punished him. However, before the punishment was sent to Nebuchadnezzar, the Lord let him know through a dream what was going to happen. In the dream, which Daniel interpreted for Nebuchadnezzar, the king was symbolized as a great tree that was cut down, and for seven years was only a stump in the ground. That meant that Nebuchadnezzar would be cut down from his power, as the tree was cut down, and that for seven years he would be without a home or a palace and would live like the beasts of the field. After the seven years had passed, Nebuchadnezzar would have learned that God was all-powerful.

For seven years, it was as Daniel had said. Nebuchadnezzar became insane and spent his days in the fields, like the beasts that grazed there. At the end of the seven years, his reason was restored to him and he recovered his kingdom and his riches.

Never again did Nebuchadnezzar turn away from the true God, whose power he had seen so vividly demonstrated in his own life.

105

The story of the handwriting on the wall

AFTER THE DEATH OF NEBUCHADNEZZAR, Belshazzar became king of Babylon. Daniel still lived there and he was still the wisest man in the kingdom.

One day Belshazzar held a great feast and invited a thousand of the lords and nobles to come and enjoy it with him.

As they were starting the feast, Belshazzar ordered his servants to bring out the gold and silver cups that his father, Nebuchadnezzar, had taken from the Temple in Jerusalem. The golden cups were brought and the people at the feast drank wine from them. As they drank, they gave praise to their idols of gold and silver, brass, iron, wood, and stone.

The feast was elaborate, and the great dining room of the palace rang with merry talk and gay laughter. In the midst of all the merriment, everyone was shocked and frightened when a man's hand suddenly appeared out of the air and wrote four strange words on the wall, where everyone could see them. The words were: MENE, MENE, TEKEL, UPHARSIN.

King Belshazzar was terrified. No one could read the language in which the words were written.

"Bring the wise men of the kingdom here quickly," cried Belshazzar to his servants. "I must know what the handwriting on the wall is supposed to mean."

The wise men soon were standing before the king.

"Whoever reads this writing and tells me what it means shall have the greatest rewards the kingdom has to offer," said Belshazzar. "I will give him a chain of gold to hang about his neck, and he will hold the third-highest position in the land."

The wise men were anxious to please the king, but none of them could read the writing. The language was strange to them. This frightened the king even more, but the queen suddenly thought of Daniel.

"Daniel has been known for many years as a very wise man," she said. "He was made master of all the wise men in Babylon during the time of Nebuchadnezzar, your father. He has the power to interpret dreams and secret meanings that are clear to no one else."

The king sent for Daniel and told him of the great reward that would be his if he could read the words on the wall and explain what they meant.

"I will read the words for you and tell you what they mean," said Daniel. "However, I want no reward and no gifts."

Then Daniel reminded Belshazzar of all the things Nebuchadnezzar had done, because God had made him great and strong. But, Daniel continued, when Nebuchadnezzar had achieved immense power, he became proud and forgot that it was God who had given him everything. For this he was punished for seven years. When he became humble again, and knew that God was the only true power, his reason and his kingdom and his riches had been restored to him.

"You knew all this," Daniel told the king. "Still, you have not acted righteously, and you have sinned against the Lord. You have taken the cups that came from the Temple of God and have drunk wine from them. You have given praise to your idols but you have not praised the one true God. Therefore these words of warning are written on your wall. It says MENE, MENE, TEKEL, UPHARSIN, which means that the Lord has tried you as king, but you have not done as you should have done, so your kingdom is to be taken away from you and the Lord will give it to the Medes and Persians."

Belshazzar kept his word about the reward, in spite of the fact that the words on the wall had been interpreted in a manner that was most terrible for him. Daniel was given a robe of scarlet, and a chain of gold to wear about his neck, and the king decreed that Daniel should be the third most powerful man in the kingdom.

That night everything happened just as Daniel had told Belshazzar it would. Cyrus the Great, a Persian general, captured Babylon and Belshazzar was killed. The army of Medes and Persians conquered the kingdom, and Darius, a Mede, was made king.

Daniel (pointing, at right) interprets the meaning of the Handwriting on the Wall while King Belshazzar and his attendants look on: Gustave Doré's engraving.

ESTHER CROWNED BY AHASUERUS

481

106

The story of Daniel in the lions' den

ARIUS LIKED DANIEL and had great respect for his wisdom and his goodness. He made Daniel the chief over all of the priests and princes of the kingdom, so that Daniel was second only to King Darius himself. This made the princes very angry and jealous. They plotted among themselves to find something evil in Daniel to tell the king. But no matter how they tried, they could discover nothing evil in Daniel.

"Unless this man does something to displease Darius in the manner in which he serves his God, we will never be able to complain to the king about him," they said.

They finally thought of a sly and wicked scheme to trap Daniel, and they went to Darius to execute their plans.

"All the princes of your kingdom ask that you make a decree, your majesty, that for the next thirty days no one may pray to any god except you, the king," they said. "Anyone who disobeys this decree will be cast into a den of lions."

Darius, who did not suspect them of evil motives, made the law and signed it. Once the Medes and Persians made a law, it could never be changed.

Daniel heard about the new law, but nevertheless he continued to pray three times a day and to give thanks to God as he had always done. The evil princes found him praying so, as they had known they would. Quickly they went to the king and told him that Daniel had been praying to God, which was contrary to the law.

"He must be cast into the den of lions," they demanded.

Darius was sorry he had signed the law, because he did not want to punish Daniel. He tried to find ways to avoid it, but toward evening the princes came to him and reminded him again that no law of the Medes and Persians could be changed. Darius had no choice but to order that Daniel be cast into the lions' den.

First he spoke to Daniel.

"Your God will protect you from the lions, because you serve Him so faithfully," said Darius. Then he went home, and spent the night fasting. He neither ate nor slept, and early in the morning he hurried to the lions' den and called out to Daniel.

"Daniel, Daniel!" cried the king. "Is your God able to save you from the lions?"

Daniel's voice came from inside the den of lions, calm and fearless.

"Yes, your majesty," said Daniel. "My God sent an angel to keep the lions from hurting me, because I have not sinned against the Lord. Nor have I done any wrong to you, your majesty."

When Darius heard these words he was very happy. He ordered that Daniel be released immediately from the den of lions. Daniel was set free,

The king comes to the lion's den and finds Daniel unharmed.

and there was no mark or injury of any kind on his body, because the Lord had protected him.

The king then commanded that the princes who had devised the wicked plot against Daniel be cast into the den of lions themselves—along with their entire families. As soon as they were thrown in among the lions, the lions attacked and killed them all.

When this had been done, Darius decreed that everyone in the kingdom must fear and respect the God of Daniel, for He was the living God and the only God whose kingdom would never end and would never be destroyed.

Daniel continued to prosper all during the reign of Darius; and after the death of Darius, when Cyrus became king, Daniel retained his high position in the land.

The angel Gabriel appears

While Daniel was in Babylon he read the words of Jeremiah, the prophet of the Lord. Jeremiah had written that after the Jews had been held captive in Babylon for seventy years they would be freed and allowed to return to their own land.

At the end of those seventy years, Daniel prayed to the Lord, and fasted. He asked that the people be allowed to go back, according to Jeremiah's prophecy. He prayed also that the city of Jerusalem might be rebuilt.

Daniel asked forgiveness for all the sins of the people, not because they truly deserved to be forgiven but because the Lord was a merciful God.

As Daniel was praying, the angel Gabriel flew by swiftly and touched him lightly.

"Daniel, I have come to tell you about the things that are going to happen," said the angel. "The Lord has heard your prayer and has sent me to speak to you. Your people will go back to their own land, as you have asked, and Jerusalem will be rebuilt. Four hundred and eighty-three years from that time the Saviour will be born, but the Jews will put him to death. Then, once more, enemies will come and Jerusalem and the Temple will be destroyed."

This was the end of the angel Gabriel's message to Daniel, and Daniel wrote it down as a prophecy of the Lord.

107

The major and the minor prophets

 ANY MEN WERE PROPHETS OF THE LORD, but not all of them wrote books of the Bible. Of the prophets who wrote down their prophecies, four are called *major prophets*. They are Isaiah, Jeremiah, Ezekiel, and Daniel, and there is a story about each of them in this volume. Twelve are called *minor prophets*. The stories of some of them are told in this volume. Here are the names of all of them:

HOSEA lived about eight hundred years before Jesus was born. He was a prophet for sixty years, during the reigns of four kings of Judah: Uzziah, Jotham, Ahaz, and Hezekiah. Hosea warned the people of Israel against worshiping idols, as they were then doing, and prophesied the destruction of the northern kingdom of Israel. This occurred only a few years after Hosea's death.

JOEL lived about a hundred years after Hosea. He was a prophet in the kingdom of Judah while Josiah was king there. Joel prophesied that the Chaldeans (from Babylon) would invade Judah; that Jerusalem would be destroyed by the Romans, many years afterward; and that the Christian Church would arise and would become great and powerful.

AMOS was a herdsman in the southern kingdom of Judah, but he was sent by the Lord to prophesy in the northern kingdom of Israel. This was during the time when Hosea was prophesying in Judah. There is a separate story about Amos, beginning on page 433, in this volume.

OBADIAH began to prophesy about six hundred years before Jesus was born. He was one of the few prophets who foretold good things to come. He said that the Jews would one day be given a wonderful land of their own, and he prophesied God's severe punishment of the Edomites (a peo-

The minor prophets: Upper row, left to right, *Hosea, Joel,
Amos.* Lower row, left to right, *Obadiah, Jonah, Micah.*

ple of a land near the land of Canaan) because the Edomites had ill-treated
the Jews.

Jonah lived about eight hundred and fifty years before Jesus was born;
some scholars believe that he was the earliest of all the minor prophets.
The story of Jonah can be found in this volume, on page 526.

Micah was a prophet in Judah during the life of Hosea. Isaiah was also
alive then and Micah confirmed some of Isaiah's prophecies about the
future sufferings of the Jewish people. The book of Micah includes some
verses that are often quoted, especially the eighth verse of the sixth chap-
ter. This verse tells us very simply and beautifully that we can please God
if we are just, and merciful, and humble before God.

Nahum lived about seven hundred years before Jesus was born. He
prophesied that the great city of Nineveh, the capital of the conquering
emperors of Assyria, would be completely destroyed. Jonah had made this
prediction also, but the people of Nineveh had repented and the Lord had

The minor prophets: **Upper row, left to right,** *Nahum, Habakkuk, Zephaniah.* **Lower row, left to right,** *Haggai, Zechariah, Malachi.*

spared them. The prophesy of Nahum came true, for the people of Nineveh later returned to their evil ways and God destroyed their city completely.

HABAKKUK lived about a hundred years after Nahum, some six hundred years before the time of Jesus. Habakkuk was one of the prophets who foretold the fall of Jerusalem to King Nebuchadnezzar and his Chaldean armies.

ZEPHANIAH lived about six hundred and fifty years before Jesus, while Josiah was king of Judah. He too prophesied the punishment of the Jews for their sins, and also the punishment of the Philistines, Moabites, Ammonites, and Ethiopians.

HAGGAI was born while the Jews were captives in Babylonia, about five hundred years before Jesus was born. Haggai encouraged the Jewish people to rebuild the Temple in Jerusalem, when Cyrus permitted them to do so, as told in the following stories.

ZECHARIAH lived at about the same time as Haggai, and many of his prophecies were made while Darius was the Persian king and ruler of the Jews. Like Haggai, Zechariah encouraged the rebuilding of the Temple. Zechariah also made prophecies concerning the coming of the Messiah, or Christ; one of his prophecies foretold the thirty pieces of silver for which Judas would betray Jesus.

MALACHI was the last of the prophets whose books are in the Old Testament; he lived about four hundred years before the birth of Jesus. Malachi prophesied the coming of the Messiah, or Christ. One of the famous prophecies of Malachi concerns the forerunner of Christ, whom Christians later recognized in John the Baptist: "Behold, I will send my messenger, and he will prepare the way before me."

After the time of Malachi, for four hundred years, there were no men known to have the inspired gift of prophesying the works of God. During that period, therefore, there are only historical records to tell what happened to the people who worshiped God.

108

The story of the rebuilding of the Temple

 HE JEWS REMAINED CAPTIVES in Babylon for seventy years, the length of time the Lord had told Jeremiah they would be held. Now, after these seventy years, a king named Cyrus ruled Persia and Babylon. The Lord made Cyrus willing to release the Jews, so that they could go back to the land of Canaan.

Jeremiah's prediction was not the only one that came true at that time. The prophet Isaiah, nearly two hundred years earlier, had foretold that a great king by the name of Cyrus would come to power and would rebuild the city of Jerusalem.

Cyrus made a proclamation and sent it to all parts of his kingdom.

"The Lord has told me to rebuild His Temple in Jerusalem. Any of the Jews who are captives here and who wish to return to their own land may go back and rebuild the Temple of the Lord, and the people of this kingdom will help them by making them gifts of gold and silver and cattle and clothing to take with them."

Almost all of the Jewish priests and Levites, and thousands of the other Jewish people, wanted to leave Babylon. The people of Babylon did as their king had commanded them and gave the Jews a great many presents. Then King Cyrus took the sacred vessels out of his storehouses—the vessels that Nebuchadnezzar had removed from the Temple in Jerusalem—and he counted them to make sure they were all there before giving them back to the prince of Judah who was going to lead his people back to the land of Canaan.

This prince's name was Zerubbabel, a descendant of King David. In all, Cyrus returned to him 5,400 of the sacred gold and silver vessels.

With Zerubbabel went 42,360 Israelites and 7,337 of their servants. They had 736 horses, 245 mules, 435 camels, and 6,720 asses. It was a huge caravan that finally arrived in the land of Canaan and reached the spot where the city of Jerusalem had once stood.

The ruins of Jerusalem There was nothing to be seen except ruins. Jerusalem was just as Nebuchadnezzar had left it many years before. The walls of the city, all its houses, and the Temple itself had been completely torn down and then set on fire.

The people immediately began to rebuild the altar of the Lord that had stood in the court of the Temple. They built it as quickly as possible, so that they would have a suitable spot at which to worship the Lord. When the altar was finished they made offerings to the Lord each morning and evening, as the people of Israel had done before their long captivity in Babylon.

Then it was time to start rebuilding the Temple itself. As Solomon had done, they hired men of Tyre to cut down cedars on Mount Lebanon and send the wood by sea to a port near Jerusalem.

Work began immediately on the building of the Temple, and when the first stones of its foundation were laid there was great rejoicing among the people. Priests and Levites played their trumpets and clashed their cymbals, and everyone sang songs of praise to the Lord.

However, there were still many very old men who had seen the beautiful Temple of Solomon that once stood on that spot, and they wept as they remembered how it had been destroyed. The sound of weeping joined with the glad cries of the younger people, and it could be heard for miles around.

The trouble with the Samaritans When the king of Assyria, Sennacherib, had conquered the ten tribes of the northern kingdom of Israel, long before Jerusalem was destroyed, he had sent people from his own land to live in the cities of the Israelites. These people were called Samaritans, and their country, once called Israel, was now called Samaria. The Samaritans worshiped idols, but they pretended to worship the Lord.

The Samaritans heard that the people of the southern kingdom of Judah had returned and were rebuilding the Temple in Jerusalem. They approached Zerubbabel and the rulers of the Jews.

Cyrus gives back the treasures taken from the Temple: A Doré engraving.

"Let us help you in your work," they said. "We too are worshipers of the Lord, and we have offered up sacrifices to Him ever since the king of Assyria sent us here."

491

They were lying, however, and the Lord made Zerubbabel refuse their assistance.

"You have nothing to do with building the Lord's house," said Zerubbabel. "We will build it ourselves, as Cyrus, king of Persia and Babylon, told us to do."

This angered the Samaritans, and they did everything in their power to hinder the rebuilding of the Temple. They even hired men to speak against the Jews to the officers of Cyrus. During the lifetime of Cyrus, they continued to trouble the people of Israel, but they were not successful.

Trouble with Artaxerxes

King Cyrus died, and a man named Artaxerxes became king. The Samaritans thought that a new king might be easily influenced against the Jews. They wrote him a letter and told him many things that were untrue.

"We think you should know that the Jews who returned from Babylon are rebuilding the wicked city of Jerusalem," the letter said. "If they finish what they are doing, they will not pay tribute to you as they should; they will undoubtedly rebel against you. The people of Jerusalem were always rebellious and were a great trouble to kings of long ago."

Artaxerxes believed the Samaritans. He inquired about the past history of Jerusalem, and he could not have been told the true story because he believed that Jerusalem had been rebellious long before that time, when actually the Jews had only been trying to defend their land from conquerors. At any rate, he wrote a letter to the Samaritans, in which he expressed his appreciation of their concern for him.

"I have learned that what you said is true," he said, "and I now give you permission to go and forbid the people of Jerusalem to continue with their building until I tell them that they may do so."

The Samaritans hurried to Jerusalem to deliver the king's message. During the lifetime of Artaxerxes, no more building was done on the Temple.

However, the people built themselves houses in which to live.

Darius and the prophet Haggai

Darius became king after the death of Artaxerxes, but the Jews did not ask his permission to finish the Temple. They had become more interested in building houses. This angered the Lord, Who sent the prophet Haggai to them.

The prophet Haggai urges the people on as they rebuild the Temple.

"You say it is not yet time to build the Temple for the Lord," said Haggai. "But is it right for you to be living in beautiful houses of your own, while His house is still in ruins?"

493

The people could not answer this.

"You have not prospered, and you have not been happy, because the Lord has not blessed you," Haggai continued. "Go up into the mountains, and cut wood for the building of the Lord's house, and He will be pleased and will bless you again."

Soon the people were busily at work again on the construction of the Temple. When the Samaritans saw what they were doing, they spoke to Zerubbabel and Jeshua, the high priest.

"Who has told you to go on building the Temple?" they demanded.

"King Cyrus long ago commanded us to come back here and rebuild the Temple of the Lord," said Zerubbabel and Jeshua.

The Samaritans then wrote a letter to Darius, the new king of Persia and Babylon. Darius, when he had read this letter, told his ministers to search through the books in which royal decrees were written, to see if what the Israelites claimed was true. He found that Cyrus had issued such a decree during the first year of his reign.

Rebuilding the Temple: Putting on the finishing touches.

The architects of the Temple consult as it nears completion.

When Darius had read this decree, he sent word to the Samaritans to leave the men of Judah alone. He told them also to give part of his own tribute, which they paid to him, to the Jews instead; and the Samaritans were to keep the priests supplied with animals for burnt offerings and with wheat, wine, and salt.

"If anyone fails to obey this law that I have made," said Darius, "timber shall be taken from his own house to build a gallows, and he shall be hanged on it. Then what is left of the house shall be torn down, until it is only a heap of ruins."

After this decree the Samaritans were afraid to trouble the people of Judah and the Jews finished building their Temple. When it was finished they held a great ceremony of dedication and offered up a hundred bullocks, two hundred rams, four hundred lambs, and twelve goats, as sacrifices to the Lord.

The feast of the Passover was celebrated during the first month after the completion of the Temple.

The story of Ezra and Nehemiah

W HILE ARTAXERXES WAS KING of Babylon, there was a Jewish priest named Ezra who had remained there after the first group of Israelites left for Jerusalem. He was a very holy man and taught the laws of the Lord to his people.

Ezra asked Artaxerxes for permission to go to Jerusalem to teach the Lord's law to the Jews who were already there. Artaxerxes not only gave Ezra permission to go, he gave the holy man gifts of gold and silver to take with him, as offerings to God, and he said that any Jews in Persia could go with Ezra to Jerusalem.

Artaxerxes did even more. He decreed that wherever Ezra went, in any of the provinces of his kingdom, the treasurers should give Ezra anything he needed—gold, silver, wheat, wine, oil, or salt. Artaxerxes did not wish to bring the Lord's anger upon his kingdom.

Ezra was commanded to select judges in the land of Judah, and to let them judge the people who would not obey the laws of God. Anyone who did not obey the law would be punished with whatever punishment those judges thought he deserved. He might be put to death, or sent away to another land, or deprived of his riches, or sent to prison.

After receiving this decree from Artaxerxes, Ezra gave thanks to God for putting kind thoughts into the king's heart. He then called together those priests, Levites, and chief men of the Jews who had remained in Babylon after Cyrus had released them. He took them to the banks of the river Ahava and told them to fast there for three days, and to pray for the Lord to show them the right way to go on their journey. Ezra had assured the king that the Lord would guard those who obeyed him, and therefore Ezra was ashamed to ask the king for an escort of soldiers to guard the traveling caravan of Jews.

Artaxerxes (with hands upraised) gives the Jews permission to return home.

Finally the Jewish people started out, with all the treasure that Artaxerxes had given them. Their wives and their little children went with them, and all along the route the Lord protected them so that none of the

497

bandits through whose land they passed could do them harm. In about four months they arrived in Jerusalem, and there they rested for three days. After that they went to the Temple and gave the silver and gold and other treasures to the priests and Levites at the Temple.

Back in Babylon, a Jew named Nehemiah was cupbearer to King Artaxerxes. This means that he carried wine or water to the king whenever the king wanted something to drink. Nehemiah heard that the people in Jerusalem were poor and very unhappy. A traveler told him that the walls of Jerusalem had never been rebuilt and were still in ruins.

This made Nehemiah himself unhappy, and he asked the king if he might go and help the people of Jerusalem to build up the walls of the city.

"How long will the journey take?" the king asked, "and when will you return?"

Nehemiah told him how long he thought it would take; this may have been two or more years, because people traveled slowly in those times. Nevertheless, the king gave him permission to go.

"One more request, your majesty," said Nehemiah. "Will you give me letters to the governors of the provinces through which I must pass, telling them to help me, and another letter to the keeper of the king's forest near Jerusalem, so that he will give me wood to make beams for the walls, and for the gates of the city?"

The Lord made Artaxerxes willing to give Nehemiah these letters, and Nehemiah set out, accompanied by soldiers and horsemen to guard him along the way.

When Nehemiah reached the provinces near Judah, he gave the king's letters to the governors. The governors themselves were friendly, but there were two men serving the governors who hated the Jews. When they learned that Artaxerxes had sent a man to help the Jews, these men were very displeased. The two men were named Sanballat and Tobiah.

Nehemiah reached Jerusalem safely and went to look at the walls of the city, to see if they were as bad as he had heard. He found the walls in ruins, just as he had been told.

The next day he called together the people of the city and told them why he was there.

"Without walls to guard your city, you are in danger of attack from our enemies," he said. "The king has given me permission to help rebuild the walls, so let us start work immediately."

"Yes, let us build the walls now!" exclaimed the people. Everyone fell to work with a will. Even the priests and the Levites helped.

Sanballat was angry. He made fun of the efforts of the Jewish people.

"These Jews are too weak to build a good wall!" he said. "Any wall they build will be so fragile that a fox that stepped on it would knock it down!"

The Jews were not discouraged. They continued to work until they had built the wall to half the height it would eventually reach. At this point it completely encircled the city.

Sanballat found that he could not discourage the Jews by making fun of them, so he conspired with Tobiah and other enemies of the Jews. They decided to attack the Jews without warning.

The walls of Jerusalem are manned

But the Jews were told of what their enemies had planned, and Nehemiah set armed men behind the wall. "Don't be afraid of these people," said Nehemiah. "The Lord will help you and we will win the victory. You are fighting for your wives, your children, and your homes!"

When the enemies of the Jews learned that the Jews were prepared to defend themselves, the attack was not made.

After that, only half of the men of Israel worked on the wall, while the other half stood guard with swords, spears, and bows. Nehemiah stationed a trumpeter to sound the alarm in case an attack should come unexpectedly.

Day and night the men worked, and the rebuilding of the wall progressed rapidly.

Unfortunately, there was trouble within the ranks of the Jewish people. There were some who were very poor and some who were very rich. The poor people complained bitterly.

"We have had to pay tribute to the king, and we have had to buy food for ourselves and our children," they said. "Now all our money is gone. We have borrowed from our richer countrymen and they have taken everything from us."

"Yes," said others. "They have even taken our children as slaves, and we have not the money to buy them back. We love our children as much as they love theirs, and we are Jews just as much as are the rich princes and rulers who have taken our children."

Nehemiah was angry when he heard how the rich had treated the poor among them.

"Give back the houses and cattle and money that you have taken from your poorer countrymen, so that they will have money enough to buy back their children," said Nehemiah.

The princes and rulers agreed to do as Nehemiah had said, and Nehemiah made them swear before the priests that they would keep their word.

Meanwhile, Sanballat and Tobiah were afraid to go into Jerusalem, because they heard that the men of Israel were still at work on the wall and that it extended entirely around the city. They still wanted to harm Nehemiah, and to get him out where they would not risk harm to themselves, they sent a messenger asking him to come out of the city and talk with them.

The plot against Nehemiah

"I am doing important work, and I cannot stop to come out and talk with you," said Nehemiah. He knew they just wanted to do him harm. Four times they asked him, and four times he refused.

Sanballat then tried another method of approaching Nehemiah. He sent a servant with a letter.

"I have heard that the Jews in Jerusalem are going to rebel against the king of Persia, and that you, Nehemiah, intend to make yourself their king," said the letter. "That is why you are so intent upon building up the wall around the city. Before I write and tell the king of Persia about this plot of yours, you had better come out and talk with me."

Nehemiah sent back an answer immediately.

"You know that what you said is not true. You are only pretending to believe these things because you are evil," said Nehemiah's letter. Then Nehemiah prayed that the Lord would let them finish the wall.

When Sanballat and Tobiah realized that they could not persuade Nehemiah to come out of the city to meet them, they hired a man in Jerusalem to frighten him. The man's name was Shemaiah. He shut himself up in his house and pretended that the Lord had given him a message for Nehemiah. Nehemiah went to the man's house to talk with him.

"Let us go to the Temple and shut the doors," said Shemaiah. "Your enemies are coming tonight to kill you."

"I am doing work for the Lord," said Nehemiah. "Should one who is doing the Lord's work stop in the midst of it, and run away?" Nehemiah knew that the Lord had not spoken to Shemaiah, and that this was just another of Sanballat's and Tobiah's schemes to hinder work on the wall. Nehemiah again prayed that the Lord would allow them to finish that work.

After fifty-two days the wall was completed and the people held a ceremony of dedication. The priests, the Levites and the people all went up to the top of the wall, in two great companies. One company went one way and the other went in the opposite direction. As they walked around the city, on top of the wall, they played on trumpets and harps and sang praises to the Lord. When the two companies met, they came down from the top of the wall and marched to the Temple, where the priests offered sacrifices to the Lord.

Nehemiah then set rulers over the city.

"Let the gates be closed at night and not opened until the sun is high in the morning," he said. "And let the men of Jerusalem take turns serving as guards, to watch over our city and warn of the approach of any enemies."

The feast of trumpets When the people of Israel were wandering in the desert, in the time of Moses, the Lord had commanded that silver trumpets be made for the priests to sound at the start of a journey. Since then, the people had celebrated the feast of trumpets on the first day of the seventh month every year.

After the completion of the wall around the city, it was time for the feast of trumpets to be held. The people asked Ezra, the prophet, to read to them out of the book of God's laws. Ezra did so, and the people were frightened, for they knew they had disobeyed many of the laws that Ezra had read. The Levites told them that this was no time to tremble and weep. This was a glad feast, and they should be happy.

Ezra taught the people much of God's law that day and the next, and the people were willing to promise that they would obey the commandments of the Lord. They wrote down all their promises on a paper, and everyone signed it.

Some time later, Nehemiah went back to Persia, as he had promised to do, and stayed for some time. The Bible does not say how long he remained in Persia, but it does say that when he returned to Jerusalem after that time, he found that the people had sinned again, and failed to keep their written promise to the Lord.

110

The story of Esther

AFTER THE TIME OF DARIUS, there was a king in Persia and Babylon named Ahasuerus.

Not all the Jews in captivity had chosen to return to Canaan with either Zerubbabel or Ezra. Many of them still lived in Persia.

In the third year of his reign, Ahasuerus gave a great feast for the officials of his court, in the garden of his palace. There were beautiful decorations all about the palace. The people at the feast drank out of vessels made of gold, and the occasion was one of great celebration.

At the same time, Vashti, the queen, gave a feast for the women of the palace.

On the seventh day of the king's feast, when he had drunk a great deal of wine and perhaps was intoxicated, Ahasuerus sent for his wife, the queen Vashti. He commanded her to come with her crown on her head, and without her veil, so that everyone might see how beautiful she was.

This was a very strange thing for a king of Persia to ask, because the women of that land, in that time, were never seen publicly without veils to cover their faces. They even lived in a separate part of the house and never appeared before men. It was considered immodest for a woman to let her face be seen by anyone but her husband.

When King Ahasuerus told Vashti to come before the crowd of princes and people of the land, so that they might see her face without its veil, she refused to obey her husband's command.

The king was wildly angry at this. He asked his wise men for advice.

"Queen Vashti has not obeyed the command of the king, her husband," said Ahasuerus. "What shall we do to punish her suitably?"

Vashti (standing, in center) refuses to obey the orders of King Ahasuerus: Doré's interpretation, which is mistaken because she never did appear before the men.

"Queen Vashti has done wrong," the wise men replied. "Now that she has publicly disobeyed her husband, all the women of Persia will think that they too can disobey. This act of Queen Vashti's is a very bad example to the other women of the kingdom."

"But what shall we do?" asked the king.

"Let us make her punishment severe enough so that the other women of Persia will not be tempted to disobey their husbands," said the wise men. "Let it be known that Vashti will never again come into the presence of the king, and let the king choose for himself another wife—one who will obey her husband as a wife should."

The king punishes Vashti
This advice pleased the king and his princes, and he did as his wise men had suggested. He wrote the decree the wise men had advised and made it a part of the law of the land. Now Vashti could never see him again.

Then the advisors made another suggestion.

"We think it would be a good idea if your majesty sent officers throughout the kingdom to gather all the beautiful young women together in the palace at Shushan," they said. "The one who pleases your majesty most, out of all the beautiful young women in Persia, can be made your queen instead of the disobedient Vashti."

"This is a very good suggestion," said the king, and he ordered his officers to go through the kingdom as the wise men had advised.

One of the officials at the palace of Ahasuerus was a Jew named Mordecai, and he had a beautiful young cousin named Esther (or, under her Jewish name, Hadassah). Esther's mother and father had died and Mordecai had taken the young girl into his own house and had brought her up as his daughter.

When the time came for all the beautiful young women of Persia to be assembled at the palace in Shushan, Esther was among them. The officer of the king who had charge of attending to the needs of the women was very kind to Esther, because her charm and beauty pleased him greatly, and he assigned her to the best part of the house where the women stayed. He also gave her seven maids to wait on her.

Just before Esther went to the palace, her cousin Mordecai gave her a word of advice.

"It is not wise to let it be known that you are a Jewess," said Mordecai.

"Very well," Esther agreed. "I will not mention it."

When King Ahasuerus saw Esther, he lost all interest in the other young

Esther is overcome as she reports to Ahasuerus the plot against his life.

women. Esther was so lovely that he fell in love with her on the spot. He

The king
chooses
Esther

placed the crown on her head and made her his queen instead of Vashti. He then held a great feast for her, called Esther's feast, and his attendants were all given presents in her honor.

Esther remained obedient to Mordecai, even though she was queen, because she felt toward him as a daughter feels toward her own father.

After Esther had been queen for a short time she had a chance to do the king a service, and it was her cousin Mordecai who gave her the opportunity.

There were two officers of the king who were angry at him for something, and they plotted together, planning to kill him. Mordecai was a watchman

The plot
against
Ahasuerus

at the king's gate and he overheard the talk about their plot. Promptly he went to see Esther.

"Two men are plotting to kill the king," he said. "You must warn him."

Esther told the king and when he checked on the story he found that the two officers were guilty. He had them both put to death for their treachery. Mordecai's action in reporting the plot was written down in the book of records, where important incidents in the history of the kingdom were noted.

111

The story of Haman and Mordecai

 HERE WAS AN OFFICIAL in the palace of King Ahasuerus named Haman, and the king had given him a very high position in the court. All of the other officials had to bow to Haman whenever he passed, because the king had told them they must. Mordecai, however, did not do as the others did. He would not bow down before Haman, because he did not feel bound to obey any law but God's.

"Why do you not obey the king's command?" the other officials asked Mordecai. They warned Mordecai that it was dangerous to ignore a royal order, but Mordecai would not listen to them.

Haman became very angry and determined to punish Mordecai. He had learned that Mordecai was a Jew, and in his anger he decided to punish all the Jews in Persia along with Mordecai. He plotted carefully and devised a scheme that would make it appear that the king himself wanted the Jews destroyed.

Haman went to Ahasuerus and spoke against the Jews.

"Your majesty, there are some people living in your kingdom who have laws of their own that are different from the laws of your people. They do not obey your laws, but only their own," Haman told the king. "It is dangerous for you to let them live. I would be glad to pay ten thousand talents into the king's treasury for the sake of getting rid of these dangerous people. I beg your majesty to issue a decree that they should all be destroyed."

Ahasuerus believed the words of Haman, his trusted servant, and he gave Haman the ring from his finger. This was the same thing as signing his name to any decree that Haman might write, because in those days a law was marked by sealing it with the king's special ring.

"I give you my ring," said Ahasuerus. "Write whatever you wish in the decree, and seal it with this ring. As for the ten thousand talents you offered, you need not pay anything at all—and you may do whatever you choose to these people."

Destruction of the Jews is decreed Haman was wickedly pleased with the success of his plan. He called the scribes—or writers—together.

"Write a decree," he commanded. "In it, say that on the thirteenth day of the last month of the year, every Jew in Persia is to be killed—men, women, and children. Anyone who sees a Jew should kill him, and whoever does so may keep for himself the Jew's house, cattle, and money."

The scribes wrote the decree as Haman had said, and Haman sealed it with the king's ring, which made it officially the law of the land. Copies were sent by messenger to the governors and rulers of every province. When the messengers had left, Haman and the king sat down to drink wine together.

When Mordecai learned of what Haman had done, he was filled with sorrow for the troubles of his people. He put on sackcloth, which was a sign of grief and mourning, and he walked through the streets uttering sad and bitter cries. He went before the king's gate, but he could not go through because no one dressed in sackcloth was allowed inside the gate.

In every province throughout the land, the Jews were unhappy. Many of them did as Mordecai had done; they dressed themselves in sackcloth to demonstrate their sorrow.

Esther learns of the decree Queen Esther had not heard about the decree, but then one of her maids told her that Mordecai had been seen in the street wearing sackcloth and mourning. Esther sent new clothing to her cousin, but he refused to remove the sackcloth.

Still Esther did not know why Mordecai was so sad. She then sent an officer of the king to go and ask Mordecai what was the matter.

"Here," said Mordecai to the soldier. "Take a copy of this decree to the queen and she will understand why I am sad. Ask her also to plead with the king to save the Jews in Persia."

The officer reported to Esther what her cousin had said, and she sent another message to him.

"It is well known that if anyone goes to the king without having been called by him, that person will be put to death, unless the king chooses to hold out his golden scepter as a sign that the intrusion is forgiven," said Esther's message. "I have not been called to the king's presence for the past thirty days. How do I dare go and speak to him?"

Mordecai sent back a second message.

"Do not think that the enemies of our people will let you live just because you are the queen," said Mordecai's message. "If you will not save the Jewish people now, someone else will save them—but you and all your relatives will be destroyed. And who knows? Perhaps the Lord made you queen just so that you would be in a position to save the Jews at this very moment."

Esther then instructed Mordecai to get all the Jews in the city to fast and pray for three days. She said, "I will do the same, and then I will go in to see the king, without having been summoned by him. If he chooses to have me put to death for this, then I am willing to die."

Esther carefully planned her attempt to save her people. She dressed herself in her royal robes, and she went to the entrance of the inner part of the palace where the king could see her as he sat on his throne. The Lord made the king feel kindly toward her, and the king held out his golden scepter, which meant that she was forgiven for entering without being summoned. Esther moved closer to the king and touched the top of the scepter, which was a sign of respect for the king.

"What is it you wish, Queen Esther?" the king asked. "Whatever it is, your request will be granted."

"If the king pleases," said Esther humbly, "I would like both the king and his minister, Haman, to come and enjoy a banquet that I have prepared today."

"Go to Haman and tell him to make ready," said the king to a servant standing nearby. "We will go to the banquet that the queen has prepared for us."

Esther's first banquet   At the banquet, the king asked again what favor Esther wanted to ask of him, because he knew that she must have wanted something very badly to dare visit his inner court without an invitation. Again the king said that no matter what she requested, her wish would be granted.

At her banquet for the king and Haman, Esther accuses Haman.

"If the king and Haman would be gracious enough to attend another banquet tomorrow, which I will prepare between now and then, I will tell the king what it is I would like to ask at that time," was Esther's reply.

510

Haman was very proud because he had attended a banquet at the queen's house and had been invited to come again next day. He passed Mordecai at the king's gate, and once again Mordecai failed to bow to him. This made Haman extremely angry, but he said nothing.

When he reached his own house, he called together his friends and sent for his wife. He wanted to boast of the honor that had been done him, and of his important position in the court.

"The king has set me above all his other servants," he bragged. "And what is more, Queen Esther invited me to go with the king to a banquet she had prepared. Tomorrow I go to another banquet at her house—and I am the only man besides the king who is invited. All these honors are very wonderful, but I cannot be truly happy about them while I see the Jew, Mordecai, sitting at the king's gate."

"Here is a suggestion for you," said his friends. "Let a high gallows be built—higher than any gallows has ever been before—and ask the king in the morning for permission to hang Mordecai on that gal-

Haman builds a gallows

lows. After Mordecai is dead, you can go to the Queen's banquet and enjoy yourself without care."

Haman was pleased with that plan, and ordered the gallows built immediately.

That night King Ahasuerus could not sleep, and to divert himself he ordered that his servants bring him the book in which important events of the kingdom were recorded. The book was brought and read to him. It happened that his servants read him the story of how Mordecai had saved the king's life by telling about the plot of the two soldiers. Ahasuerus asked what reward had been given to Mordecai for this.

"No reward was given him, Your Majesty," his servants answered.

As they were speaking, Haman came into the court. He had come to ask the king's permission to have Mordecai hanged in the morning, but before he had a chance to say anything, the king spoke.

"Tell me, Haman," said Ahasuerus. "What do you suggest that I should do for a man whom I want very much to honor?"

Haman immediately jumped to the conclusion that the king referred to himself, and he proceeded to tell the king of the kind of honor that would appeal most to him.

"Let the man whom the king wishes to honor be dressed in the king's

At the king's command, Mordecai is led in triumph through the streets.

royal robes, let him ride the king's horse, and let the king's crown be set on the head of the man the king wishes to honor. Then let one of the noble princes lead the horse on which the man is riding through the streets of the city, and call out that this is the king's favor to a man he wishes to honor."

"Very good!" said the king. "Now, take the robes, and my horse, and my crown, and go to Mordecai, the Jew. Let it be exactly as you have said. You may lead the horse through the town and call out that this is the king's favor to a man he wishes to honor."

Mordecai is honored Haman did not dare disobey the king, but he was humiliated and angry that he was forced to show such honor and respect to a man he hated. After Mordecai had ridden through the town on the king's horse, dressed in the royal robes, and wearing the king's crown, he returned humbly to his seat outside the gate. Haman hurried home as quickly as possible, hiding his face in shame. He told his wife and friends of the embarrassment he had suffered, and as he was speaking a messenger came to take him to the banquet that Esther had prepared.

Haman is hanged on the high gallows he built for Mordecai.

This time when the king asked her what request she had to make of him, Esther answered him fully.

Esther's second banquet
"If the king is pleased with me, and wishes to grant my request, then let him save the lives of all the Jews, and my life as well. Evil things have been said about the Jews— things that are untrue—and an order has been issued that I and all of my people are to be killed."

King Ahasuerus was astonished, for he knew nothing about the decree that Haman had issued and sealed with the royal seal.

"Who has dared to do such a thing?" he demanded.

"This man, Haman," said Esther. "He is our enemy."

Haman was terrified, and the king was so angry that he left the room. Haman fell on his knees before Esther and begged for his life. When the king came back into the room, that was the position in which he found Haman. A soldier of the king spoke at that point.

"Outside of Haman's house is a gallows seventy-five feet high that Haman built to hang Mordecai," said the soldier.

***The high
hanging
of Haman***
The king ordered that Haman himself be hanged on the gallows he had built for Mordecai's execution, and when Haman had been hanged, the king was able to forget his anger.

Although Haman was dead, the decree that he had sent to all parts of the land was still in force, because once a decree became a law of the Medes and Persians, it could not be changed. Even the king himself could not change it, but he told Esther and Mordecai that they might issue another decree to save the Jews, and seal it with his royal seal, so that this too would become a law.

Mordecai quickly assembled the king's scribes and gave them a new decree to write. This decree said that all Jews had permission to gather themselves together on the thirteenth day of the last month of the year— the day on which their slaughter had been scheduled by Haman—and defend themselves against anyone who tried to harm them. They were given permission to kill any attackers with swords.

When the news of the second decree became known, there was great rejoicing among all the Jews. Messengers were sent to ride as fast as pos-

***The feast
of Purim***
sible to all parts of the land, so that all people would hear of the decree in time. Then the Jews armed themselves, and fought for their lives, and won the victory. Then for two days, on the fourteenth and fifteenth days of the twelfth month, they rested.

After that, they celebrated a feast each year on the fourteenth and fifteenth day of the last month. This feast is called the feast of Purim, and to this day the Jews celebrate it every year.

112

The story of Jonah and the big fish

I N BIBLICAL TIMES, THE CITY of Nineveh was a great metropolis. It was in the country of Assyria.

In the city of Nineveh there were beautiful temples, and large palaces, and many houses. It was a big city, and thousands of people lived there.

Walls a hundred feet high encircled Nineveh, and they were wide and thick enough so that three horse-drawn chariots could drive around on top of the walls, side by side. Fifteen hundred towers, each one two hundred feet high, were built above the walls. From these towers guardsmen could shoot their arrows at any approaching enemy.

Nineveh was a rich and beautiful city, but the people who lived there were wicked and the Lord determined to punish them. Before He did so, however, He wanted to warn them and give them a chance to repent of their sins.

The Lord chose a man named Jonah to go and tell the people of Nineveh about the punishment they were sure to suffer for their sins. When He spoke to Jonah, however, Jonah was afraid to go; and Jonah thought he could escape from the command of the Lord by running away. He fled to a seaport not far from Jerusalem and booked passage on a ship that would take him to a far-distant land.

After Jonah's ship had sailed out to sea, the Lord caused a violent windstorm to sweep across the waters, and the ship was in grave danger of being broken to pieces. The sailors were all frightened and prayed in terror to the various idols they worshiped. They threw part of the cargo overboard, trying to make the ship lighter, but still the ship appeared to be in serious trouble and the storm continued to rage.

A great storm comes up and threatens the boat in which Jonah travels.

Everyone on board was frightened except Jonah. Jonah was asleep in the ship's cabin and did not even know there was a storm blowing. At length the captain of the ship went to where Jonah was sleeping and awakened him.

"How can you lie there sleeping when the ship is almost ready to break in pieces?" the captain demanded. "Get up and pray to your God. Perhaps He can save us!"

Jonah and the ship's captain returned to where the other men of the crew were talking.

"Someone on board has sinned wickedly," said one of the men. "This storm has been sent because of him."

Jonah is thrown into the water

"Let's cast lots and find out which one of us is the sinner," said another man. They all felt certain that this was a sure way to determine which man was responsible for the trouble, and this time it proved to be the case, for the lot fell to Jonah.

"Who are you?" they asked him. "What terrible thing have you done to bring this storm upon us?"

"I am a Hebrew," Jonah answered. "I am running away from the voice of the God who made all things—the earth, the sea, and the sky, and all the people of the earth."

"Why are you running away from the voice of your God?" they asked wonderingly. "And what can we do with you, so that this dreadful storm will stop before we are all killed?"

"Throw me overboard, and the waters will be calm for you as soon as you are rid of me," said Jonah. "I know very well that this danger has come to you only because I am here."

The sailors did not want to throw Jonah into the sea, and they rowed hard, trying to reach land, but the storm was too strong and they had to give up. They still dreaded the idea of throwing Jonah to what seemed certain death by drowning, and they all prayed to the Lord for forgiveness.

"Please do not punish us for what we must do," they prayed. "If you have sent the storm because of him, then we must cast him overboard."

No sooner had Jonah been thrown into the sea than the storm stopped and the waters were calm.

A big fish swallows Jonah God did not intend that Jonah should drown. He had sent a great fish alongside the ship, to swallow Jonah as he hit the water. Jonah remained inside the fish for three days and three nights. During that time he prayed constantly to the Lord and repented of his wrongdoing in trying to flee from the voice of the Lord.

God heard Jonah's prayers and caused the fish to cast Jonah out on the dry land by the seaside. Then God again commanded Jonah to visit Nineveh and warn the people of God's intention to punish them for their wickedness. This time Jonah obeyed.

Nineveh was such a large place that a man could walk for three days in going from one end to the other of the city. Jonah waited until he had walked within the city for one full day, and then he made the proclamation God had commanded him to make.

"Nineveh is to be destroyed in forty days," he called out in a loud voice. "Nineveh will be destroyed because of the people's sins!"

The people of Nineveh were sure that God must have sent Jonah. Immediately they began to mend their ways. They repented of their wickedness and prayed to the Lord for forgiveness.

The big fish casts Jonah up on the shore.

The king of Nineveh issued an order that everyone must fast and pray. "Let everyone turn away from sin and repent," he said. "Perhaps if we are penitent, the Lord will forgive us."

Jonah preaches to the people of Nineveh and prophesies their destruction.

Throughout the city, then the people obeyed the king's decree and prayed humbly for the Lord's pardon. God saw their changed ways and heard their prayers. He did not destroy the city because it was not evil any more.

This angered Jonah.

"I am shamed before all these people," he exclaimed. "I told them that the Lord was going to destroy them all after forty days, and my prophecy did not come true! I was afraid this would happen, because I knew all along that the Lord is merciful. As for me, I would be better off dead now. I wish the Lord would let me die!"

The Lord spoke kindly to Jonah, in spite of the fact that Jonah was guilty of an unforgiving spirit and should not have said such things.

Jonah could not bear to remain in Nineveh. He went outside of the city to stay for a while, so that he might be near enough to see what happened there. He built himself a booth, or shelter, and sat under it in the shade.

The Lord made a large vine grow up over Jonah's booth in a single day,

Jonah retires under the miraculous tree and his heart is softened.

to give him ample shade, and to keep him cool in the heat of the day. Jonah was very grateful for that vine. He did not know that it was just part of a lesson God intended.

The day after the vine had grown up over Jonah's booth, God sent a worm to gnaw at the vine and make it wilt. Then God caused a hot east wind to blow, and made the sun burn down on Jonah's head until he was overcome by the dreadful heat.

Once again Jonah cried out that he would be better off dead.

The Lord then showed Jonah how the vine had been intended as a lesson to him.

If Jonah felt sorry about the destruction of the vine, which had grown in a single day, should not the Lord feel even more sorry at the thought of destroying a great city that had been built for years, along with thousands of innocent babies and helpless animals? This was the lesson that the Lord gave Jonah.

Jonah understood then, and was ashamed.

113

The story of Tobias and his journey

THE BIBLE WAS TRANSLATED INTO LATIN nearly sixteen hundred years ago by St. Jerome, one of the great scholars of ancient Rome. St. Jerome's translation is called the Vulgate, which means that it was written in the language of the people (of Rome).

There were fourteen books or parts of books that St. Jerome called the Apocrypha, meaning the "hidden, or secret, books." The famous English translation called the King James version, which was published in 1611, included the Apocrypha; but most editions of the King James version printed in the last hundred years have not included them. Catholics include eleven of Apocrypha's fourteen books and sections as inspired and sacred parts of the Bible.

The Apocrypha are part of the Old Testament, and like the Old Testament as a whole they include some poetry, some history, some stories of the adventures or experiences of people who were faithful to God, some prayers, and some prophecy. Included are three sections in the book of Daniel and six chapters in the book of Esther. Others are:

THE BOOK OF TOBIAS and THE BOOK OF JUDITH, about which you can read on the following pages.

THE BOOK OF WISDOM, also called THE WISDOM OF SOLOMON, which is a book of moral and religious advice, following the Proverbs.

ECCLESIASTICUS, also called THE WISDOM OF JESUS (or JESHUA) THE SON OF SIRACH, another book of advice.

THE BOOK OF BARUCH, a book of prophecy and prayer, written by a friend or follower of the prophet Jeremiah.

Two books of history, covering a period just before the Christian era, when a family named the Maccabees or Machabees ruled over the Jewish people.

*The three
other
sections*
Of the other parts of the Apocrypha, which are not accepted as inspired, two are additional books of Esdras or Ezra (which are simply different ways of spelling the same name). They tell more about the rebuilding of the Temple of Jesusalem, about which you can read on pages 485 to 501.

Finally there is the Prayer of Manasseh. The Bible does mention a prayer made by a Jewish king of that name, but this is not accepted as being the same prayer.

*Tobias
and his
troubles*
Tobias was an Israelite, a descendant of Naphtali, one of the sons of Jacob who founded the Twelve Tribes of Israel. Tobias lived almost three thousand years ago, at the time when the wicked King Ahab was ruling in the kingdom of Israel.

At that time Ahab often fought wars against the kings of Assyria, and in these wars the kings of Assyria would often capture Jewish people. Tobias was captured in this way and taken to the Assyrian capital, Nineveh. Captives with him were his wife and his young son, whom he had named Tobias also—we would call the boy Tobias, Jr.

Most of the Jewish people who were captured worshiped the idols of the Assyrians and disobeyed other commandments of God, but Tobias and his family continued to worship God only and obey His laws.

For some time Tobias prospered. At one time he was so prosperous that he deposited ten talents of silver—worth at least ten thousand dollars—with a man named Gabael, a banker in the city of Rhagae or Rages, about 350 or 400 miles away from Nineveh.

But then Tobias's troubles started. Because he buried his kinsmen when they died, and burial was against the laws of the Assyrians, the king of Assyria sent men to arrest him. Tobias fled from the city, and the king seized all his property. Later Tobias was able to return to Nineveh, but he became blind and could not earn a living, so the family lived on a small amount that Tobias's wife earned and they were very poor. Tobias was very unhappy, and he prayed to God for help.

The prayers of Tobias and Sara

On the same day that Tobias was praying, another prayer was being offered up to God by a faithful but unfortunate young woman in a far-off town called Ecbatana.

The young woman's name was Sara. She was the daughter of an Israelite named Raguel, who like Tobias was a captive far from home but had continued to worship and obey God. Sara was a good and religious girl, but she was the victim of a wicked demon named Asmodeus. Seven times Sara had been married, but every time Asmodeus had killed her new husband immediately after the ceremony, so she had never been able even to begin married life with any one of the seven. She too prayed piously to God for help against this demon. People were beginning to think she murdered all her husbands!

God heard both prayers, Tobias's and Sara's, and He sent the angel Raphael to earth to help them both.

Just at this time, no doubt through inspiration sent by God, Tobias remembered the large amount of money he had left with Gabael. If he could get that money he and his family would not be poor any more. So he called his son to him.

By this time young Tobias had grown almost to full manhood. He was old enough to marry and old enough to make the long journey to Rhagae. His father told him about the money.

"Go to Rhagae and collect the money," old Tobias told his son. "Hire a man to go with you and I will pay him wages."

Young Tobias dutifully went out to look for a man, and of course the first man he found was Raphael. He could not know Raphael was an angel, and Raphael said his name was Azariah and that he was an Israelite, a kinsman of Tobias; he had in truth taken the appearance and person of the real Azariah, for the purpose of this mission. Old Tobias was delighted with this choice of a companion for his son, and soon the disguised angel and the young man set out together for Rhagae.

When the two travelers came to the great river Tigris, young Tobias

Raphael (standing) tells Tobias to save parts of the fish. A Doré engraving.

went to the bank of the river to wash himself and a big fish leaped out of the water and attacked him. Tobias was frightened and cried, "Help! Help me!" but the angel calmly said,

"Take hold of the fish and pull it on shore."

524

Tobias did this and was surprised to find it easy. He and Raphael made a meal of the fish. Then Raphael said,

"Now cut out the heart, the liver and the gall bladder of the fish and keep them."

Tobias did this, but he soon became curious and asked,

"Azariah, what are these parts of the fish for?"

"If you are troubled by an evil spirit," Raphael replied, "burn the heart and liver and the smoke will drive the spirit away. As for the gall bladder, that will cure blindness."

Tobias and Sara are Married

After a few days the travelers came to the city of Ecbatana, which lay on the road from Nineveh to Rhagae, about halfway between them. Here they stayed with Raguel (for he was of the same people and religion), and Tobias fell in love with Sara; but he was afraid to marry her because he had heard about her seven previous husbands, all of whom had immediately died.

"Don't be afraid," Raphael told him. "When you take your wife to the bridal chamber, put some hot ashes on the heart and liver of the fish, to make smoke. And you and your wife must both pray, and God will save you."

Then Raphael spoke, as representative of old Tobias, to Raguel, the father of Sara, for that is how marriages were arranged in those times. Raguel was delighted and gladly gave his daughter to young Tobias, and they were married almost at once; but Raguel still feared that this new son-in-law would die like all the others. He even dug a grave to put Tobias in.

Sara was even more frightened, and cried. But when she and Tobias went to their room, Tobias made the smoke and they both prayed, as Raphael had told them to, and the demon fled far away; but Raphael, using his supernatural powers, followed him and bound him so that he could do no more damage.

The next morning Raguel sent a maid to the room of the newly wedded couple, fully expecting to find Tobias dead. When he heard that Tobias was still alive he was so happy that he arranged for two weeks of feasting. While this was going on, Raphael went alone to the city of Rhagae and collected the ten talents of silver, which he brought back to young Tobias. Then all three of them went back to Nineveh.

Raphael reveals himself

Before they arrived, Raphael told young Tobias, "Remember to have the gall of the fish in your hand and put it on your father's eyes."

Old Tobias was so happy to have his son home safely, with a new wife, that he wept; and while he was weeping young Tobias put the gall on his eyes and the old man rubbed them and rubbed away the film that had made him blind.

They still did not know that Raphael was an angel, but they were so grateful to the man they called Azariah that old Tobias offered him half of the money he had brought back. But Raphael said,

"Do not pay me anything. Instead, give thanks to God. For I am the angel Raphael, whom God sent to help you."

Then they fell on their knees and praised God. Raphael disappeared, and neither old nor young Tobias ever had need of his help again, for they lived good lives and long lives.

114

The story of Judith and Holofernes

UDITH WAS a beautiful and pious woman of Bethulia, a city of the Jews, who saved her city from an army of Assyrian invaders.

The Assyrians were commanded by a general named Holofernes. He had a fearsome army, and he had already conquered several parts of the Jews' land of Judea, together with several surrounding lands. All the people were terrified, and although they prayed to God to save them they lost their faith that even the Lord could overcome such a great army.

Now, Judith had been a widow for more than three years, for her husband had died of a sunstroke during the harvest; and Judith had worn rough clothing and had not made herself seem attractive, because she was in mourning. But when her city was threatened she left her house and went to the leaders of the city, at the head of whom was a man named Uzziah, and she said to them,

"You can be beaten only if you lose faith in the Lord; for He can do anything. Tonight I will go out from the city, and with the Lord's help I will save the city."

Ussiah and the other elders, or leading citizens, were so desperate that they were happy to do anything that might save them. They said to Judith,

"Go, then, and may the Lord be with you."

Judith made herself very beautiful, with fine clothes and jewelry and perfumes. Then she prayed to God for help. And then, taking her maid with her, she went to the gates of the city (for in those times all cities were protected by great walls and gates).

Judith was so beautiful that Uzziah and the other elders gasped with admiration when they saw her. They opened the gates and Judith went fearlessly to the camp of the enemy army. There she asked to see the commander, Holofernes, and because of her beauty and her apparent wealth she was taken to him at once.

To Holofernes and the other Assyrians, Judith said that she had left the city of the Jews because she did not wish to be destroyed with its other people. They believed this, and that night she was invited to a banquet given by Holofernes.

Judith would not eat the food offered her by Holofernes, because the Jews had very strict religious laws concerning the foods they could eat and the way it must be prepared. Instead, Judith ate food that she had brought with her and that her maid served to her.

"But you will soon run out of food," said Holofernes, "and then what can we give you to eat?"

"My food will last as long as you live, my lord," Judith answered; but

Judith enters the tent of Holofernes.

Judith carries the head of Holofernes back to her city, to prove his death.

Holofernes did not understand her meaning. He thought she meant that God would continue to provide her with food.

For four days, Judith lived in the camp of the Assyrians while they prepared to attack the city of Bethulia. Each day Judith prayed to the Lord, and each night she ate her own food at the banquet of Holofernes.

On the fourth night all the other guests left early, so that Judith was alone with Holofernes. She took a sword, prayed to God for strength, and cut off his head. Then with her maid she returned to Bethulia.

When the Assyrians found that their commander had been killed, they first believed that the Israelites had been able to attack them; and this caused such fear among them that they fled from the valley in which lay Bethulia, and the city was saved.

Judith was a great heroine among the people of her city, and her success caused them once again to have faith in God to save them from their enemies.

115

The story of Susanna and the Elders

T HE PROPHET DANIEL PROVED WHEN HE WAS still a very young man, little more than a boy, that he had great wisdom and also was blessed with God's favor.

In Babylon, the city to which Daniel had been taken by King Nebuchadnezzar (as told in Story 26), there lived a beautiful young woman named Susanna. She was good as well as beautiful, and she was fortunate besides in being married to a rich man, whose name was Joakim.

Among the Jewish people living in Babylon were two elders who were greatly respected by the people and who had been appointed judges. In reality these elders were not good but wicked men. They wanted power over Susanna, and together they went to her and threatened her.

"If you do not submit to us," they told her, "we will tell all the people that we saw you meet another man in your garden, which would be unfaithful to your husband Joakim."

Susanna was in despair. "There is no hope for me, even though I am innocent," she said, groaning; "for the people will surely believe these men, who are elders and judges, instead of me." Nevertheless she was both courageous and good and she refused to submit to the elders.

The elders carried out their threat. They accused Susanna of misbehavior, and though Susanna denied it the people believed the elders.

At this point God caused Daniel to feel the holy spirit that was in him, and Daniel came to the defense of Susanna.

"You have condemned this woman without a fair trial," he told the people.

So great was Daniel's reputation for wisdom that the people gladly listened to him and did what he asked. Daniel asked only that he be able to question the two elders—not when the elders were together but when they were apart. The people agreed and separated the elders so that neither could hear what the other said.

To the first, Daniel said,

"When you saw this woman in the garden with the strange man, what kind of tree were they under?"

"A mastic tree," the elder replied.

Then Daniel had the first elder sent away and called the other to him.

"Under what kind of tree did you see them?" he asked again.

"Under a liveoak tree," the second elder replied.

As Daniel had supposed, the elders had not gone so far in their false story as to agree on small details.

After this, the people could not think evil of Susanna. She was declared innocent and Daniel was highly praised.

Daniel speaks, Susanna is set free, and the elders are bound instead.

116

The story of Bel and the Dragon

NOTHER OF THE ADDED PARTS of the book of Daniel tells how Daniel outwitted the priests of one idol, or false god, and destroyed another false god.

This happened when Daniel had become a great and famous man. Cyrus, one of the most famous kings of ancient history, was king in Babylon at that time and he liked and trusted Daniel more than any of his other courtiers and advisers.

The Babylonians, including the king, worshiped idols. Daniel worshiped only God. Also, he knew that the idols were false gods, merely statues and not gods at all.

The chief god of the Babylonians was called Bel. He was served by priests, and every day they took to him many bushels of flour for bread, and forty sheep for meat, and a full cask of wine for drink. The king and the people of Babylon believed that the god Bel actually ate and drank this much daily.

One day the king said to Daniel, "Why don't you worship Bel, as we do?"

"He is only an idol," Daniel replied. "I worship only the living God, Lord of heaven and earth."

"How can you say Bel is not a living god?" the king asked. "Just think of what he eats and drinks every day!"

At this Daniel laughed. "He never ate anything," Daniel assured the king. "He is only clay inside and bronze outside."

This made the king angry. He wanted to believe in Bel, but he trusted Daniel also. He called the priests to Bel to him and said,

"You must prove to me that Bel actually eats the food you supply to him. If you cannot prove it, you will die; but if you can prove it, Daniel must die."

The priests—there were seventy of them—agreed to this, and so did Daniel. They all went to the big room of the temple in which the statue of Bel stood, and the priests put the food and drink on the table before Bel. Then the priests left. The king intended to seal up the room so that no one could possibly get in or out without breaking the seal. Before leaving the room, Daniel and his servants scattered fine ashes on the floor around the table and the statue.

Then Daniel left the room, and the king sealed it, and they went home.

Of course, there was a secret entrance to the room, known to the priests and to no one else. Every night the priests and their wives and children went into the temple by the secret entrance and had their dinner from the food that had been put there for Bel.

Footprints in the ashes The next morning the king went back to the temple, attended by Daniel. First the king satisfied himself that no one could have tampered with the seals he put on the doors. Then he broke the seals and opened the doors. All the food and wine was gone from the table!

The king was convinced. "You are great, O Bel!" he cried.

But Daniel laughed. "Look at the footprints," he said.

The king looked. "I see footprints of men, women, and children!" he exclaimed.

It did not take long for the king to find the secret door. So the priests were killed and Bel was destroyed. But the king still worshiped idols.

The king also worshiped an enormous serpent, or snake, that was kept in the temple. It was probably nothing more than a boa constrictor or python, one of the giant snakes that we often read about today, but in that part of the country such big snakes were not known and the people called it a dragon and thought it must be a god.

"You cannot deny that this is a *living* god," the king said to Daniel.

"I do not deny that it is living," Daniel replied; "but one cannot kill God, while I can kill this serpent easily."

"You have my permission to try," said the king.

Daniel made a concoction of pitch and fat and hairs and fed it to the big snake. The concoction swelled up inside the snake until it burst and died.

This convinced the king, but the people were so angry that they forced the king to have Daniel put in a den of lions. There were seven lions in the den and they were given no food, but God did not let them touch Daniel, and God even sent the prophet Habakkuk to take food to Daniel in the lions' den.

Daniel remained in the lions' den nearly a week. On the seventh day the king came to the lions' den. Actually he intended to mourn for Daniel, who had been his friend. It did not occur to him that Daniel might still be alive. But Daniel sat calmly in the den. He was not even hungry.

Finally the king was convinced. He acknowledged the greatness of God and Daniel was again the most favored and most powerful man in Babylon.

In Story 29 you can read how Daniel was placed in a lions' den under another king, Darius, and came to no harm because he had God's protection.

Daniel (bending over) shows the king the footprints.

535

117

The story of the three guardsmen

THE TWO APOCRYPHAL BOOKS OF ESDRAS tell more about how the Temple was rebuilt at Jerusalem, about five hundred years before Jesus was born, and they tell how a young man named Zerubbabel won the favor of the mighty Persian king Darius and became the governor of Jerusalem.

At that time Jerusalem was ruled by the Persian empire. Jerusalem had been conquered and destroyed more than fifty years before and most of the Jewish people had been taken as captives to Babylon and other places in the Persian empire. But even while these Jewish people were not allowed to return to their homeland (for fear they would again become strong and be able to make war against the Persians), they were permitted to live in comparative freedom and several of them rose to high positions in the governments of the Persian kings. Young men of Jewish families were educated and trained for positions of leadership the same as young men of other nationalities.

In the second year of his reign, Darius gave a great feast in his capital city of Nineveh and invited the governors of all the many provinces in his vast empire.

One night during the period in which the feast was under way (for such a great occasion might last for weeks), Darius was sleeping in his room. Outside his door, to guard him, were three young men of his bodyguard. One of these young men was Zerubbabel, a member of a noble Jewish family.

The three young bodyguards, who had to be awake all night, decided to take a problem and see who could answer it best; and they agreed to show their answers to Darius and ask him to reward the wisest of them.

536

Esdras (or Ezra) praying while the Temple at Jerusalem is being rebuilt.

The question they selected was, "What is the strongest of all things?"
The first guardsman wrote, "Wine is strongest." The second wrote, "The king is strongest." The third, who was Zerubbabel, wrote, "Women are

Assembly of the Jews in the capital of Darius, to hear Zerubbabel speak.

strongest; but truth is mighty and will prevail"—that is, the truth can con-
quer anything.

All three placed their written answers under the king's pillow, so that he
would see them when he awoke. When Darius did awake and read the
answers he assembled all his governors and famous guests and then he
summoned the three young guardsmen.

"Now," said Darius to the guardsmen, "explain to us why you answered
as you did."

The first to speak, the young man who had answered "Wine," said,

"Wine is strongest because it affects men's minds and makes them think
things are not as they actually are. If wine is stronger than men's minds,
it must be stronger than men themselves."

Next to speak was the guardsman who had answered, "The king." He
said,

"Surely men are strongest of all things on earth, since they rule the land
and the sea and all things on them; and since the king is master of all men,
the king must be the strongest of all things."

Now it was Zerubbabel's turn to speak.

"Women are more powerful than men," said Zerubbabel, "because no matter how powerful a man is, he will let himself be influenced by the woman he loves. This is true even of the king himself.

"But even more powerful than women is truth. For nothing can change truth. Wine cannot change it, men cannot change it, the king cannot change it, women cannot change it. Truth never dies; it lives forever. No man can dispute with truth. Blessed be the God of truth!"

Then all the assembled rulers shouted, "Yes, truth is the strongest!" And Darius said to Zerubbabel, "You have won and have proved yourself wisest. Sit next to me, and you shall be called my kinsman, and whatever favor you ask of me I will grant."

At once Zerubbabel asked as his favor that the city of Jerusalem should be rebuilt (for at that time Jerusalem still lay in ruins), and that the treasures takes from Jerusalem should be restored to it.

Darius rose, and kissed Zerubbabel, and gave orders that Zerubbabel should be escorted safely to Jerusalem and that all the governors of all the provinces should give him supplies and other help in rebuilding the city.

Soon afterward, Zerubbabel assembled a large group of Jews who had been living in exile in Persia, the country of Darius; and Zerubbabel led his group back to Jerusalem, where they rebuilt the city.

118

The story of the Maccabees

FOR MORE THAN FIVE HUNDRED YEARS, the Jewish people were ruled by foreign kings. During only one period of about one hundred years did they have kings of their own. These kings were members of a family called the Maccabees.

You will remember that the Jews had been made subject to the kings of Persia—such great kings as Cyrus and Darius. But about three hundred years before Jesus was born, an even greater king arose in Greece. He was called Alexander the Great, and he conquered not only the Persians but nearly all the civilized world that was then known to the people who lived near the Mediterranean Sea. But Alexander respected the religions of other peoples and did not destroy Jerusalem or the Temple as other conquerors had done. The Jews willingly paid taxes to Alexander and many of them joined Alexander's army and fought for him.

Unfortunately, Alexander died when he was a very young man and the kings who came after him were not so favorable toward the Jews and their religion. Under these later kings, the Jewish people entered a long period of great suffering.

It is true that for a time the Jews continued to be faithful to God and God continued to protect them. When one of the great kings, Seleucus, sent a general named Heliodorus to destroy Jerusalem and the Temple, God sent His angels to beat Heliodorus until he was unable to carry out his purpose and the city was spared. But a later king named Antiochus did destroy Jerusalem and ruin the Temple, and also he persecuted those who still worshiped God and obeyed his laws. Many faithful Jews became martyrs, or men who suffer and die for their faith.

The martyrdom of Eleazar.

One of these martyrs was a priest, Eleazar. He was beaten to death because he would not eat pork (for it was then a religious law of the Jews, and is still a religious law with many Jews, that pork may not be eaten).

Even more horrible was the death of seven sons and their mother. One by one, each of the sons was offered a choice: He could eat the flesh of swine (that is, pork), and go free; or he could refuse, in which case he would be tortured to death. One by one the seven young men refused, and one by one they were put to death, each time with all the surviving brothers and their mother watching. Many of the tortures were too cruel to describe. The seventh and last son was the bravest of all—not only because he had seen all six of his brothers tortured and knew what would happen to him if he refused, but also because he was offered a very important position as a nobleman if he would desert God and serve Antiochus. Nevertheless he refused and was killed, and then his mother (who had urged him not to submit to the king) was also put to death.

When this persecution of the Jews began, a young Jewish leader named Judas Maccabeus, with eight or nine followers, fled to the mountains and

The martyrdom of the seven brothers before their mother.

lived there. They lived "in the manner of beasts," eating what food they could find and sleeping in the open. Judas Maccabeus was the son of a rich and noble priest named Mattathias. This priest had five sons, of whom Judas was the third oldest. Because Mattathias was so influential among the Jews, the cruel king Antiochus offered him great wealth and power in return for submission, but Mattathias refused and led a revolt against Antiochus. The revolt did not succeed, but neither was it wholly beaten down; and when old Mattathias died he had a large body of followers who were willing to fight the armies of Antiochus.

On the death of his father, Judas Maccabeus (which means "Judas the Hammerer") came out of hiding and became the leader of the Jewish army.

Judas was a brilliant military leader, and in addition he was a devout man. Before every battle he and his entire army prayed to God, and fasted as a sign of worship. Once Judas led his army of only six thousand men against an army of forty-seven thousand and won a great victory. He attacked several cities that had been captured by the Syrian armies of Antiochus, and he recaptured and freed these cities. By the time he was

Judas Maccabeus restores the services in the Temple.

ready to recapture Jerusalem, his enemies were so afraid of him that they retreated and he marched into Jerusalem without opposition.

Judas Maccabeus was so successful that his enemies had no choice but to make peace with him. Judea, the land of the Jews, became an independent country with Judas Maccabeus as its king; and though Judas was killed in battle only two or three years later, his brothers and then their sons and grandsons and descendants were kings over Judea for a hundred years. These were the Maccabee kings.

But finally the Roman Empire became so powerful that no nation was able to withstand it; and about sixty years before Jesus was born, after a hundred years of Maccabee rulers, Judea along with all nearby countries became mere provinces of Rome. After that time there never was an independent nation of the Jewish people until the modern state of Israel was founded.

The death of Antiochus (see page 541).